WE
ARE
mother
ABRAHAM

DR DEB WATERBURY

Published by Deb Waterbury, LLC

ISBN 9781700151797

Library of Congress Control Number: 2019918140

Printed in the United States of America

Scripture quotations are referenced as notated within text

FOR SPENCE AND MILES,
MY BOYS
AND MY HEART

PROLOGUE

If you were to ask just about any mother what her number one struggle is, she will invariably land on that painful and unavoidable dilemma of when and how to let go of her children.

Mothers everywhere can attest to the ease with which they can protect, provide for, nurture, and love their children. However, bring up the heartache of letting her children fail or painfully learn a lesson or the absolute worse—get hurt—well, I don't know a mother out there who finds that easy. On the contrary, it's extraordinarily hard.

If you've been there, then you know this pain intimately. It can bring sleepless nights, lost relationships, despair, and hopelessness. Where do we go when we find ourselves here? Is there comfort or explanation to be found anywhere?

We Are Mother Abraham is the story of motherhood in its most raw form. The title came to me many years ago when God called me to make this sacrifice with my own son. I found myself face down in my office one day in absolute despair over this sense of helplessness when it came to my son. He seemed lost, and there was nothing I could do. I thought I might go insane with the pain of it all.

In the middle of my sobbing, I began to hear a name over and over in my head, "Mother Abraham." After hearing it so many times, I eventually stopped and asked who in the world that was. After all, there's no such person as Mother Abraham. Everyone knows it's Father Abraham. Still, I was desperate for some direction, so I got up and read Genesis 22 where Abraham was called to sacrifice his son, Isaac.

I knew the story well, and after reading it again, I asked God what that had to do with the strange name I felt He had been repeating in my head. It was then that

God began to speak to me.

He told me that Sarah was also called to this same thing. We don't read about that part in the Bible, but when Abraham took Isaac up to Mount Moriah for the sacrifice, chances are very good that Sarah knew what her husband intended.

And still, she had let him go.

That, in and of itself, would be unthinkably difficult, but then God started reminding me of the love of a mother for her child. He reminded me that this bond is all but unbreakable, as well as the need to protect them from all harm. Sarah had to deny all of that to let her son go, just as all mothers are called to do the same.

This brought me no comfort at first, but then God began pouring His love onto me, reminding me of how favored we were in His eyes as mothers. God trusts mothers enough to give them such a high calling. He made our natures those of nurturing and love, and He made us strong enough to deny those natures when it came time to give those children back to Him.

That's where I found my comfort.

Mother Abraham.

What God showed me was that there is a supreme and tremendous call on the heart of every mother, and it will tear at the very fabric of what she was created to do. However, our Father also made us strong. He made us fearless, and He made us capable. We are Mother Abraham, and believe it or not, there is honor in this call. There is favor. And there is love.

THE CORD

BY AMY MERRICK

We are connected, my child and I, by
an invisible cord not seen by the eye.

It's not like the cord that connects us 'til birth.
This cord can't be seen by any on earth.

This cord does its work right from the start.
It binds us together, attached to my heart.

I know that it's there, though no one can see
the invisible cord from my child to me.

The strength of this cord is hard to describe.
It can't be destroyed; it can't be denied.

It's stronger than any cord man could create.
It withstands the test, can hold any weight.

I am thankful that God connects us this way.
A mother and child, it will not go away!

CONTENTS

* | CHAPTERS OF *MOTHER ABRAHAM*

CHAPTER ONE

The telephone buzzed next to Katherine's bed. She rolled over to see the bedside clock, though she hadn't been sleeping. It read 1:23 a.m. The knot in her stomach turned into that familiar sick ache. Oh God, not again. Please, not again.

CHAPTER TWO

The smell of antiseptic floor cleaner was almost nauseating. Katherine stared at the stark white tile beneath her feet and took a deep breath. The doctor hadn't come out yet, and it had been an awfully long time. She couldn't remember it taking this long before. She could hear the clap, clap, clap of the cleaning lady's cart as it rolled past her, its loose wheel protesting loudly in the otherwise empty hallway. Katherine fought the urge to tell the woman to ease up on the floor cleaner just a bit. She could swear that her nose was going to start bleeding at any moment from the noxious fumes. She looked up in time to see a sleepy-eyed Ken coming down the hall carrying two Styrofoam cups of vending machine coffee.

"I don't want that," she said without making eye contact with him.

"Yeah, me either," he answered, sighing heavily. "But I think we both need a jolt of something, don't you?"

He held the cup out to her, and she took it, again without looking at him. Her husband had been here before, too, and they both felt the same exhaustion and frustration. Still, neither talked about it, at least not right then. Maybe it was because they were too tired, or maybe it was just too painful to talk about it…again. For Katherine, the thought of speaking the same words out loud for what seemed like the umpteenth time would have possibly been the straw that broke the proverbial camel's back. She just couldn't, at least not now, so they sat in uncomfortable silence until they heard footsteps approaching from down the hall.

Ken stood up first, hand extended to the doctor making his way toward them. Katherine stood slowly, robotically, still not looking up. She felt like she might be sick at any moment.

"Mr. and Mrs. Matthis?" the doctor asked as he shook Ken's hand. They both nodded, so he continued. "I'm Dr. Combs. Your daughter is stable. The paramedics administered an opioid antagonist called Naloxone, or Narcan."

"We're familiar with it," Katherine interrupted, but the tone in her voice made Ken give her a sharp look. He wasn't a fan of her attitude at the moment.

"Yes, well, Naloxone was administered on scene, which is primarily why your daughter is still with us," Dr. Combs continued. "Nicole suffered respiratory arrest after ingesting a large number of opioids along with alcohol. There is significant indication that Nicole has been abusing at least some form of opioids for an extended period of time. With this abuse, her body is becoming less and less capable of bouncing back after taking too many, especially when she combines them with other sedatives, like alcohol."

Katherine was only half listening. She'd heard it all before, and part of her was in distress over her lack of distress at the moment. Shouldn't she be more upset? Shouldn't she be feeling at least some kind of sadness or worry or even anger right now? Because she wasn't feeling any of that. Instead she was just tired.

"There are a number of different options for treatment centers," the doctor went on. Ken was taking notes, but Katherine had a hard time even paying attention. She wanted to sit down. She didn't want to hear this, not again.

Instead, she found her mind going back to the days when Nicole was playing soccer in middle school. Katherine remembered thinking then that her life was too busy, with trying to get Nicole to her soccer games and practices, running Tommy all over the city with baseball practice, all while grading papers and leading the Fellowship of Christian Athletes club at the high school where she taught eleventh grade history. Ken helped where and when he could, but his job as a marketing consultant at one of the largest cell phone distributors in the country kept him at work for long hours and on the road almost as much. She tried not to complain, though. The money was really good, but his schedule left her to play single parent most of the time.

Nicole was a natural at sports, always had been. She was athletic and confident, scoring the most points at whatever sport she happened to be playing. Soccer, however, was her favorite, and all of her coaches kept saying what a future she had in the sport if she kept at it through high school. She made good grades, had lots of friends, and pretty much seemed like any normal twelve-year-old. Tommy, her younger brother, bugged her, like all younger brothers should, but she loved him. She went to every one of his T-ball games that she could, and she cheered him on with veracity.

If there were any signs that Nicole was going to end up where she did, Katherine missed them entirely. Sure, Nicole was driven, and sure, she was a perfectionist. She never wanted to fail and got really upset when she did. Katherine even remembered a time when Nicole was about seven that she cried all the way home from the eye doctor's office when the doctor inadvertently said that she had "failed" her eye exam and needed glasses. Nicole latched onto the word, "fail," and it took Katherine an hour and two ice-cream cones to get her daughter through that one.

It seemed that the word "fail" just had no place in Nicole's vocabulary. Katherine always saw this as a good trait though, not a bad one. She felt that this trait would spur Nicole on to greatness. Had it been one of the indicators that Nicole would end up where she was? The thought nagged at Katherine, even as she continued to remember when it all seemed to go bad.

High school hadn't worked out for Nicole the way she or Katherine had hoped. She tried out for the soccer team as a freshman, and she made the squad, but this didn't seem to be enough for her. She didn't understand why should wasn't playing. She sat on the bench for the entire first season, and there was no consoling her.

Ken and Katherine tried to explain that she had to earn her place on the starting lineup and that the fact that she wasn't playing at the moment didn't mean she wasn't a good player. It just meant that she was still a freshman. Of course, it didn't help their argument that there were two other freshmen players who managed to be on the field at least once every game, and this fact did not escape Nicole's attention.

Interestingly, however, this didn't motivate Nicole to get better. Instead, it seemed to de-motivate her, causing her to pull away from the sport and anything even remotely athletic. She didn't even bother to try out for the team as a sophomore, and by the time she was a junior, she seemed to lose interest in sports altogether. Her grades began to suffer, and eventually the friends she hung out with began to look nothing like those she'd been friends with before.

Not that Katherine would know. Nicole stopped bringing her friends home. As a matter of fact, Nicole was seldom home herself. Once she got her driver's license, she was gone almost every night on the weekend, and because Ken and Katherine had never had any trouble from their daughter, they didn't think much of it. They didn't like her new clothes or the fact that she didn't seem to like anyone in her family anymore, but chalked it up to "teenaged angst" and left it at that.

As Katherine thought about it later, she realized that they simply didn't want to see. Who wants to admit that their child might be heading down the wrong road? They knew her! They'd raised her, and they had raised her to be responsible, loving, and moral. They needed to convince themselves this was all just a phase and that Nicole would snap out of it eventually.

But eventually never came.

Katherine tried everything. She tried spending more time with her, even if Nicole protested the entire time. She tried mandatory curfews, which were largely ignored. She and Ken tried grounding Nicole, taking away privileges, and taking away her favorite things. They tried making her go to church functions and joining the high school group at church. They even forced her into going on a missions trip to Nicaragua with the youth group, but nothing worked. She just seemed to pull further and further away from them. She even stopped paying attention to Tommy, and the pain on her son's face every time his big sister missed one of his games was torture for Katherine.

What had they done wrong? What were they not doing right? Ken and Katherine spent countless hours asking themselves these questions, but still the answers eluded them.

Nicole managed to maintain good enough grades to graduate, but just as soon as she graduated, she moved out. She did enroll in the local community college, but Katherine had no idea what she was studying. She didn't stay in college long, anyway, dropping out after only a year. Nicole continued to keep them at arm's length, and no matter what Katherine did to try to insert herself back into her daughter's life, nothing worked.

Nicole was nineteen years old when they got the first horrible phone call that she had been in an automobile accident. It turned out to be a DUI with Nicole driving under the influence of both alcohol and other drugs. She spent the night in jail, had to go to court, and was eventually slapped with huge fines and a pretty little ignition interlock device on her Ford Escort. She had to endure the embarrassment of breathing into that little gem for a year before her car would start.

Nicole seemed very contrite after that. She moved back home, and things looked like they might turn around for a brief period. Unfortunately, it wasn't long before their daughter started sinking into that familiar place once again, a place where apparently Katherine and Ken were not allowed to go. Less than a year later Nicole was arrested again for possession of an illegal substance and landed in a court-mandated rehabilitation center.

Once again Katherine allowed herself to feel some measure of hope. Maybe this would be the thing that would get through to their daughter. Certainly, Katherine never imagined herself one of those parents who went to visit their child in rehab once a week, but she never missed an opportunity to see Nicole. She wanted Nicole to see that she was supported, no matter what she did, and loved even more than that.

Katherine couldn't say if she went out of guilt or shame or love or devotion. It was more than likely a combination of all four, but she continued to go until Nicole was finished with the program eight months later.

Again, Nicole moved back in with them for a brief time, but within three months of her moving out for the third time, she was back in trouble, once again for a drug-related offense. They bailed her out of jail for the third time, took her home for the third time, and tried getting her the help she needed for the third time Katherine couldn't shake the feeling that somehow this was all her fault, and consequently, it was hers to fix. She tried new treatment facilities, new methods of talking with Nicole, new groups, new anything. Surely, she would eventually land on the right thing.

Katherine also never gave up praying, but she began to feel that even that was useless. Was God even listening? Why wasn't He helping her with her daughter? She prayed and she prayed and she prayed some more. But Nicole moved out again, got in trouble again, and the merry-go-round went round and round and round. Eventually, Katherine stopped praying about Nicole altogether. It simply hurt too much.

A year later they got a call from the hospital after Nicole overdosed for the first time. She was living with some guy they hadn't even met, and it was he who called them from Corner Mountain Hospital. Katherine hardly remembered talking with the young man, but Ken later told her she was pretty rude to him. She quite frankly didn't care, and she told Ken as much. That boy represented everything wrong with her daughter, and being kind to him was not tops on her priority list.

It was obvious that their daughter needed more help, but for the life of them, they couldn't think of something else to do. Katherine knew she had to do something, however, so she found another rehab center, raised the money they needed to send Nicole to it, and away she went. Nicole didn't stay, though. After about three months, Katherine got a call from the center saying that Nicole had disappeared and that their strict policy regarding runaways would preclude her from returning.

Katherine thought about looking for her, and she did go to the apartment Nicole had shared with that horrible boy, but it was empty. No sign of Nicole or the young man. Katherine didn't know where else to look, but she did drive around the area for a little while, just hoping to catch a glimpse of her daughter. She didn't, so she returned home, exhausted and nauseous. She had to do something, but she couldn't think of what that might be.

The feeling came close to driving her insane. She stopped eating or doing much of anything. Her only saving grace was that it was June when this happened, so school was out for the summer. Ken didn't know what to do for his wife, much less his daughter, so he withdrew even more into himself. Tommy spent most of his afternoons in his room with the door shut. He couldn't stand being around his parents anymore. Their house had become a den of sadness, and Katherine was in the center of it all.

"What do you think, honey?"

Katherine was vaguely aware of her husband's voice somewhere in the distance, but in her mind she was still back at their house, sitting at the kitchen table trying to figure out what to do for their daughter.

"Katherine? Katherine, did you hear what Dr. Combs said?"

Katherine looked up dreamily to see the two men staring expectantly down at her. At some point during the last few minutes Katherine had sat down. She didn't remember when, but now she found herself looking up at Ken and Dr. Combs while trying desperately to remember what the doctor had said that she was supposed to have an opinion about.

"Dr. Combs thinks Nicole needs to be in a treatment center," Ken explained, tired of waiting for Katherine to respond to his question.

That snapped Katherine out of her stupor. "A treatment center?!" she exclaimed. "You mean to say she needs another treatment center, Ken! It's not like we haven't tried that—a bunch of times!"

"Keep your voice down, Kate," Ken said, putting his hand on her shoulder in an attempt to calm her. Katherine hated when he spoke to her like she was a child, and she hated feeling like she was in this alone.

"Get your hand off of me, Ken!" she said through gritted teeth, "and don't talk to me like I'm emotionally compromised."

Ken let his hand drop and took a half step back. Dr. Combs looked both ways down the hall to be sure their now heated discussion hadn't brought any additional onlookers.

"We've tried treatment centers, Dr. Combs," Katherine was now addressing the doctor personally, "and this is where we still are. I fail to see how one more is going to make a difference."

"Mrs. Matthis," Dr. Combs began, "I understand your frustration, but you have to understand that your daughter is an addict."

That word hung in the air like the smell of rotten meat. Katherine winced.

"And with addiction, recovery will always involve relapse. That's why we never give up. We just keep trying, hoping that the next one is the right one, that it's the right time."

Katherine knew in her heart that he was right, but she needed to do something. Giving her daughter's life and healing up to someone else seemed wrong. She was Nicole's mother. It was her job to protect her, to love her, to help her, for crying out loud! How could she give that over to someone else, especially when all of those "someone elses" had failed so far?

"Why don't you go home and think about it," Dr. Combs suggested soothingly. "No decisions need to be made right this moment. Nicole will need to stay overnight to be sure she is breathing well on her own. Come back in the morning. Barring any unforeseen contingencies, your daughter should be released then, and you can discuss her options with her yourselves."

Katherine was looking at the floor, tears blurring any chance she had of seeing the doctor clearly.

"Thank you, doctor. We'll come back in the morning," Ken said.

"Wait," Katherine blurted out. "Can I at least see her first?"

"Of course," Dr. Combs said. "They've taken her upstairs to Room 412, but please don't stay long. All of you need rest." With a wan smile, he walked away.

Katherine looked down the hall for the elevator sign. She saw it toward the end of the hall to their right and began walking without even looking to see if Ken was following. She found herself irritated with him pretty much all of the time these days, and tonight was proving to be no exception.

Ken did follow her without so much as a word, and they both entered Room 412 a few minutes later. Nicole was laying there, a tube down her throat and machines hooked up all around her. Katherine could hear the monotonous beeping of the cardiac monitor next to the head of Nicole's bed, and the tears came before she could even think. Her daughter looked so small in that hospital bed. Katherine could clearly see that sweet, innocent twelve-year-old for the first time in years, and she was overwhelmed with a sense of failure. It was her fault Nicole was there. She hadn't been a good enough mother, and now her daughter was suffering for it. She was overwhelmed with a grief so poignant that she had a hard time standing for a moment.

Ken had moved around to the other side of Nicole's bed and was holding her hand. Katherine looked at her husband, a tear sliding down his own cheek, and the weight of responsibility hit her again. Guilt and pain and regret filled her to the brim, and she thought she might burst from the weight of it. She could also feel herself sliding toward despair, but she didn't have the faintest idea of how to stop it. She was losing her daughter, and every instinct inside of her screamed that she couldn't let that happen.

But how to stop it? What could she do? Where could she turn?

As she stood staring at her unconscious baby girl, the dark curtain she was trying to keep at bay gently slid over her heart.

03

CHAPTER THREE

Neither of them noticed the tall orderly who had come in while they stared helplessly at their child in that hospital bed. Neither of them noticed the pain on his own face as he watched, and neither of them noticed when he slipped out again.

Instead of noticing him, Katherine gave in to the pain that would change her life forever.

"Would you like some eggs for breakfast," Katherine asked her daughter.

"I don't know about her, but I want some!" chimed in Tommy from the next room. Nicole made no move.

" Nicole? Did you hear me? I asked if you would like some eggs." Katherine had a hard time keeping the edge out of her voice. After opting out of a treatment center for the time being, her daughter had been home with them again for about three weeks after her latest stint in the hospital. Whereas the first few days were alright, laden with the all-too-familiar guilt-ridden Nicole that always followed one of these episodes, the last few had taken them back to where they always ended up—face-to-face with the sullen Nicole that acted like they all got on her last nerve.

"I heard you, Mom. I just don't want any."

Katherine stopped whipping the eggs for a second and sighed exasperatingly. "Would it kill you to say so?" she mumbled.

Nicole rolled her eyes and kept her head down over the book she was reading.

Tommy came bounding into the kitchen, plopped himself at the table on the seat next to his sister, and started talking even before his bottom hit the cushion. "So, Sis, my game is at four o'clock this afternoon at Corner Mountain Park. I'm playing first base today since I pitched at the last game. But that's okay 'cause I need to get better at stretching for the ball. You know, I can't pitch every game, so I have to be a good first baseman, too." Short breath, and then, "You're coming, right? Please say you're coming! Please, please, please!!" Though her brother was sixteen by now, he seemed to regress to that needy eight-year-old when it came to his big sister.

A smile was playing over the corner of Nicole's mouth. Her brother's infectious spirit was just that—infectious. "I'll try, Pain-in-the-Butt."

"Aw, don't say you'll try. That means you won't come. I need you to be there, Sis! I play better when you're there." Tommy was smiling now. He knew how to play his sister, even if she wasn't around as much as he wanted.

She threw a piece of napkin at him and said, "I'll try, okay? I mean it. I really will try to come."

"We'll be there," Katherine interjected. "I know your sister wouldn't miss it for the world, would you, honey?"

"Like I said, I'll try," Nicole said, with an unmistakable attitude this time.

"Oh, alright," Tommy conceded. He got up, started to leave, but stopped abruptly and gave Nicole a side shoulder hug. "I love you, Sis."

Nicole patted his arm and said, "I love you, too, Pain."

After a few uncomfortable moments, Katherine asked, "So, what are your plans for the day, sweetheart?"

Nicole shrugged.

Katherine, unwilling to be deterred, continued, "I was thinking you might want to go with me to Bible study this morning. We're in between studies, so today is just a social thing. I know the ladies would love to see you."

"I don't think so, Mom."

"Oh, come on, Nicole," Katherine continued. "You need to get out, and it won't kill you to be nice for a change." She wished she hadn't said those words almost the second they came out. She just couldn't help herself. Nicole was so exasperating, and taking a passive aggressive dig at her daughter came more naturally than she'd like to admit.

Without a word, Nicole got up from the table and headed upstairs. A few seconds later Katherine heard the door to her room slam. Actually, it was the room that used to be Nicole's. It now served as a makeshift office for both Ken and Katherine, but they had been sure to put a hide-a-bed sofa in there on the off-chance Nicole came home. The funny thing was that no matter how long it technically wasn't her daughter's bedroom anymore, Katherine never stopped calling it "Nicole's Room."

She finished up in the kitchen, her mind a blur the entire time. Where had things gone wrong? She could still remember the fun times she and her daughter used to have together. Sure, Nicole had gone through the normal teenaged rebellion from mom, but for the most part, they got along well. That is, until all of the changes really took hold. In retrospect, Katherine could now see that these changes came when Nicole started experimenting with drugs. That's when she started to withdraw from the family, from her friends, from the church, from anything that represented her old life. That's when Katherine started to lose her.

That knot in her stomach grew more pronounced as she reminisced. The truth was that Nicole was never far from her mind, no matter where she was or what she was doing. Katherine was always thinking of her daughter. Somewhere down deep she knew that this obsession with making Nicole's problems her own was unhealthy, but she couldn't help it. She felt so responsible. She simply felt like she had failed Nicole, and somehow, she had to make it right.

Her eyes cleared, and Katherine realized that she had been wiping the same four-inch section of the kitchen counter for twenty minutes. She no more wanted to go to her ladies' group that morning than she wanted to go upstairs and talk to Nicole some more. However, this was their social week, and Katherine had stupidly signed up to bring plates, napkins, and cutlery. They couldn't eat all that casserole and guacamole without plates, now could they? She thought briefly about dropping the stuff off at her friend, Marlene's, house, but she knew that Marlene would simply guilt her into going anyway.

Katherine wiped her hands on the hand towel, took off her apron, and headed up the stairs to change for her meeting. Tommy was taking a couple of summer school classes, so he had already left. She stopped in his room to gather up his dirty clothes lying conveniently on the floor. After picking those up, she went back into the hall and got to Nicole's closed door. She stopped for a moment and listened. She couldn't hear anything, but that wasn't unusual.

Nicole stayed quiet most days, lost in her own music while keeping her earbuds in her ears. Katherine wanted so badly to open the door and talk to her daughter. She longed for the times when she could do that. But she also knew that Nicole was in no mood to talk to her. As a matter of fact, Katherine was pretty sure that Nicole would leave again soon. The pattern was so clear, and they were already on that downward spiral.

Instead of knocking on the door, Katherine continued down the hall to her own bedroom to change. Her stomach hurt dreadfully, but the truth was that she couldn't remember when it didn't hurt these days. She couldn't remember the last time she smiled either.

***

The Tuesday morning Bible study group at Corner Mountain Community Church was in its fourth year of meeting together. It began as a small group of women meeting in one of their living rooms and grew to a thriving group of about thirty women who now had to meet at the church. Katherine had been attending Corner Mountain for about ten years, and she knew these women well. They had been through thick and thin together, but even though she knew most everything going on in their lives, the other women knew little about Katherine's.

Katherine had always considered herself a strong woman who could take care of her own stuff. At least that was the reason she used whenever she briefly considered sharing things with the group, particularly as they related to Nicole, and then decided against it. The truth was, and she knew it, that she didn't want to share about Nicole because she felt like such a failure as a mother. The other ladies knew that there were issues with her daughter, but they knew little to no specifics. Marlene knew, since she was Katherine's closest friend, and then there were maybe three other women she felt she could trust, but Katherine refused to share her Nicole-problems with the group.

"You're being prideful," Marlene would tell her.

"No, I'm not," Katherine would protest back. "I just don't think everyone needs to know my stuff, or my daughter's stuff, for that matter."

Marlene always harrumphed at about this time, leaving her friend to contemplate what she'd said. Marlene knew better than to push Katherine. Nicole came by her need for independence very naturally.

Consequently, Marlene knew all about what happened to Nicole three weeks earlier. Her heart went out to the Matthis family, especially to her friend, Katherine. With four children of her own, Marlene knew firsthand the pain that children can bring to the heart of any mother.

"How ya holdin' up," Marlene asked Katherine softly as the two of them set out the paper plates and napkins.

Katherine shrugged. "Okay, I guess. I just don't know what to do. I feel like I'm losing her again, and I don't know what to do to stop it."

Marlene put her arm around Katherine's waist, giving her a little squeeze. "I'm praying for you, my friend. I wish I knew what to do or say to make it better."

"Me, too," Katherine said with a wink. "Me, too."

"Welcome, ladies!" It was Susan Bishop, the leader of their group. "If you could all find your seats, we'll get started. I know we are all ready to dig into all that amazing food you've brought, but there are a couple of housekeeping items I need to take care of first."

Chairs started scooting all over the room as the women began to sit. Marlene and Katherine made their way to a table near the back of the room. That's always where Katherine preferred to sit, just in case she got a phone call about Nicole and had to make a hasty exit. They were joined by Katherine's other close friends, Alison Cordell, Marianne Bonheight, and Beth Williams. There were short hugs and greetings all around the table when Sarah began addressing the group once again.

"Well, thank you all again for coming today. We had such an amazing study this last eight weeks, diving headfirst into the book of James." There were stifled words of agreement all over the room. "It was such a good study that I really prayed strongly over what I felt we should look at next." Susan picked up a book from the podium and looked at it contemplatively before going on.

"You see, we generally stick to books of the Bible in these studies, but I felt God moving me toward something different this time. This book came across my path some six or so months ago, and it sat on my bedside table for most of that time. But about three weeks ago, I picked it up and started reading, and the comfort I received was nothing short of mind-boggling."

She looked out over the thirty or so sets of eyes staring expectantly at her before going on.

"It's just so hard to be a woman sometimes, am I right?" she asked the group, and a strong chorus of "Amens" followed her question.

"Yes, I thought so." She smiled and continued. "I think it's also hard to be a mother, possibly the hardest thing about being a woman at times." Another chorus of "Amens," even louder than the first.

"All of us in this room are mothers or are looking to be some day. Some of us are even grandmothers by now, and whereas I'm not a fan of a lot of studies out there on motherhood, this one is so spectacularly different that I feel compelled to present it to you all now for our next study." She turned the cover of the book around so that the entire group could see it. "It's called, Mother Abraham."

The ladies in the audience began to titter and talk softly about such a strange title.

"Mother Abraham?" one woman asked out loud. "Isn't it Father Abraham?"

"Yes, it is," Susan answered, "but this book isn't about Abraham. This book is about Sarah."

She saw all of the bewildered faces, so she continued. "It's about Sarah, but in the context of how Sarah had to sacrifice Isaac, not Abraham. It's about the call on her life to give up her only son, though every instinct she had was to protect him at all costs. It's about that kind of call on all of us as mothers." Susan paused for a beat to let that sink in. "This book is told from Sarah's perspective, so in that sense, it's historical fiction, something we don't generally read in this study. However, I think the time for this study is now. I believe the Lord has much to teach us about the beauty and strength of who we are as women and mothers, and I can only tell you that my heart has changed completely since finishing it myself."

Katherine had gone numb. She was absolutely in no place to read a book like that. She could feel Marlene's stare, but she refused to acknowledge it. Katherine just looked ahead, waiting impatiently for the moment when she could get out of that room.

Marlene reached over and took Katherine's hand in hers. "Don't bolt, girl."

Good night! This woman knows me too well!

Susan was still talking, but Katherine was no longer listening. She could feel small beads of sweat breaking out on her forehead, and Marlene held her hand tighter.

"I have copies of the book up here for you to purchase. We'll start the first chapter next Tuesday. But for now, let's see," she said, as she looked out over the room, "Kelly, would you pray over our food?"

Katherine didn't hear Kelly's prayer. She was thinking about that blasted book and how she was going to get out of attending this round of Bible study. Suddenly she was aware of the sound of chairs scooting against the tile floor.

"Earth to Katherine. Come in, Katherine." It was Marianne. "Where are you right now?"

"Nowhere," Katherine answered with a slight smile. "Just daydreaming, I guess."

"I'm looking forward to this one, aren't y'all?" asked Beth in her Alabama drawl. "I don't know about y'all, but I need a little encouragin' when it comes to that young'un of mine."

"Me, too," said Alison. "Besides, it might be nice to get lost in someone else's story for a little while." They all giggled at that, all except Katherine. She was busy gathering up her stuff, intending to make a quick getaway.

"You leaving?" asked Alison.

Katherine didn't make eye contact but kept moving. "Yes, I'm afraid so. I've got so much to do. I really just came to bring the plates and napkins."

The four women exchanged knowing glances but said their good-byes anyway.

"We'll see you on Sunday then, Katherine," Beth said as she, Alison, and Marianne made their ways to the food table. Marlene, however, stayed at the table, unwilling to let Katherine just leave.

"What do you have to do that's so pressing?" she asked as Katherine started putting her jacket on.

"Just some things," Katherine answered, again without eye contact. "I'll see you later, Marlene." And then she was out the door.

Marlene watched after her for a moment and then headed toward the front of the room where Susan was busy selling books to the ladies.

"Hey, Marlene," Susan greeted her when it was her turn. "How are you doing? How's the new grandbaby?"

Marlene brightened. "She is perfect! The best thing about being a mother is being a grandmother!"

"I couldn't agree more," Susan said. "You need a book?"

"Actually, I'll take two," Marlene answered. "I'm buying one for a friend." You're not getting off that easy, sweetheart, she thought. She fully intended to drop a copy off at Katherine's house later that night.

04

CHAPTER FOUR

$\mathcal{N}$icole pretended to listen to music and look through her Rock Girl magazine until she heard the door close, indicating that her mother had finally left the premises. There were all kinds of reasons why she didn't want to necessarily be around her mother, but today, Nicole really needed her mother to leave already. She kind of smirked at the thought of going to her mom's Bible study with her this morning. Like that was going to happen!

Today, however, it was about more than that. Nicole had been okay being at her parents' house immediately following the hospital. This wasn't her first scare after mixing the wrong kinds of drugs, but that didn't make it any easier. She needed to recuperate, and for a little while, she actually believed what she told them. Maybe she even wanted to believe that she was going to go straight and stop the drugs for good. It didn't take long, though, for all of those insecurities to rear their ugly heads, especially being at home.

She had long since lost the idea that she belonged in this house, a member of this particular "perfect" family. She decided that was a pipe dream she was no longer going to torment herself with quite a while ago. Tommy had always been the "good son," and well, she never could seem to measure up. Eventually, after entering high school and realizing that she wasn't going to be the soccer star everyone said she was going to be, it was easier to stop trying. That's when her old friends also became reminders of her failures, so she began seeking out friends who wouldn't make her feel so much like a failure. It was while hanging out with this new crowd that Nicole first discovered beer.

She sure didn't like the taste, at least not at first. What she did like was how it made her feel after she choked a few down. Everything seemed unimportant then. She didn't feel as insecure, and she stopped feeling like a failure. She felt good for the first time in a long time. Consequently, when she had another opportunity to drink, she jumped at it. Before long, Nicole was named among the "party girls" at Corner Mountain High, and that identity fit. She couldn't fail if she wasn't trying, and that suited her just fine.

Of course, her parents noticed the change in Nicole, but they didn't know what to do about it. Especially not her mother. Nicole withdrew more and more from the family, and even though she occasionally felt badly about her mom, she also didn't want the merry-go-round of trying to please her and everyone else on the planet either.

She graduated and made a run at community college, but then eventually ended up sharing an apartment with three of her friends and working at a local coffee shop. All of that was interrupted occasionally, when she found herself in and out of rehab. During all of that, she almost never saw her parents—on purpose. And then one fateful day, she met Adrian.

She'd seen him around, mostly at the bars where she and her friends hung out when she wasn't working. He was tall and cute, and there was a definite sense of danger about him that piqued her interest from the start. He always looked like he was checking everyone out, suspicious of every move the people around him made. She would tell him later that he always looked like he was running from something or someone, continually looking over his shoulder. The truth was, Adrian was always running from someone, mostly the cops.

Nicole began asking around about him and learned that he hung out at the bars because he supplied most of the patrons with a myriad of drugs—from "X," better known as "ecstasy," to harder stuff, like cocaine and heroin. The fact that he was a dealer should have scared her, and in her former life, it would have. Now his profession served only to make her more interested. He was all that the old Nicole would have avoided, which in her mind could only mean that the new Nicole should go after him with all she had.

And that's exactly what she did.

Throwing caution to the wind, Nicole asked a friend to introduce the two. Adrian was kind of aloof at first, not really giving her the time of day. But Nicole was a very beautiful girl, standing at about five foot eight inches tall, blonde, and trim. Adrian wasn't able to resist her for long, and very soon they became an item.

Adrian lived fast and wild, and he didn't mind taking Nicole along for the ride. She didn't mind either, at least not at first. It was exciting to be with someone who had so much money, who lived on the edge all of the time, and who could get her anything her heart desired. Nicole eventually began experimenting with a lot of other drugs, all supplied by Adrian, and she sunk lower and lower into a life that would make her parents throw up if they knew.

She was partying with Adrian and a bunch of her friends when she landed in the hospital this last time. It did sort of bother her that none of them came to check on her. Only her parents did, but she also knew that her friends couldn't get caught in the state they were in. And Adrian was always on the lookout for the police, since there were multiple warrants out for his arrest at any given moment. Nicole knew it was silly to have expected them to visit, but she couldn't help but be a little hurt that no one did.

Nicole had been home for two weeks when she heard from Adrian for the first time since the overdose. Her parents had tried to take away her phone, but she reminded them that she was twenty-five years old and that she paid for the thing herself. They had no right, though her mom made a pretty good case for, "While you're living under my roof…," and so on. In the end, however, Nicole managed to keep her phone and it was a text from Adrian one night that began the downward spiral that Nicole knew she was on again.

"Hey, Baby," he purred into the phone.

Nicole looked at the clock on her nightstand. It read 2:34 a.m. "Adrian?" she asked through the fog of sleep. "Adrian, is that you? It's two-thirty in the morning, for crying out loud!" she whispered as forcefully as she could. She tried to sound indignant, but she was actually ecstatic to hear the deep timbre of his voice on the other end of the line.

"I know what time it is, Baby," he continued to purr, "but I miss you. I wanted to check and see how you were doing."

She could hear the playful smile in his voice, and even if she had wanted to, she wouldn't have been able to stop the tingle on her arms at just hearing him. She didn't want to.

"I miss you, too," she said sheepishly, trying to keep her voice soft so that she didn't wake anyone up.

"I figured you were just about ready to break outta there by now. There's a party happening at Mick's place this weekend, and you are not going to want to miss it, sweetie. It's going to be epic!"

Nicole was still living in the fear and pain of this last overdose, so another party truthfully sounded awful to her. However, the thought of seeing Adrian masked the sick feeling she had at the notion of partying. "I don't know, honey," she began. "I don't know if I want to do that anymore. I almost died, you know?"

"Yeah, but you didn't, did you?" he answered back. "You're too young and too hot to die, Baby Girl. I've told you that before. Dying from too much fun happens only to losers, and you are not a loser."

She giggled, despite the hesitation she felt. She really did miss him. "I know. You've told me that before."

"So, what do ya say," he continued. "When can I come and break you outta that joint?"

"Give me a week, Adrian. I feel bad leaving so soon. They did take care of me and everything." Nicole was feeling that old nagging sensation in the pit of her stomach again, the one that showed up when she began reminiscing about home and the way things used to be. She missed her family sometimes, as much as she hated to admit that. Being in her old room was actually comforting, if she were to tell the truth. But then remembering how far she had sunk and how much of a disappointment she had become, the need to escape came pouring back into her brain before she could even think about it. That guilt and remorse were always enough to push her right back to where she knew there would be no guilt or judgment, back to Adrian and the life she'd taken as her own so many years ago.

"Okay, Baby Girl, a week. In a week I'll give you another call, and then it's me and you again, just like it ought to be." He said a few more things about missing her, things that made her stomach tingle along with her arms, and then they hung up. Nicole lay wide awake the rest of the night, mostly trying to figure out why she wasn't more excited at the prospect of running off with Adrian again. Truth be told, she was feeling a sense of dread, but why?

The problem was that she totally forgot all about that feeling pretty much as soon as she got out of bed the next morning. Her mother and father were downstairs in the kitchen, ready to ambush her for the millionth time. They were sitting at the kitchen table, coffee cups in hand, literally staring at her when she came in. She almost turned around and went right back upstairs, but her mother interrupted her impulse.

"Good morning, Nicole. Your father and I would like to talk with you about some things."

Nicole looked at her dad questioningly. She knew that the one wanting to talk with her was her mother. She and her dad had already talked about a lot of things, as had she and her mom, but her mom just couldn't leave it alone. She just kept picking and picking and picking, like she thought if she picked long enough, she would find the right spot and Nicole would relent. Nicole was irritated before she spoke her first words.

"About what?" she asked, and the attitude in her voice wasn't lost on her mother.

Her mom took a deep breath, trying to calm her nerves. "We want to talk with you about your plans after this."

Nicole sat down across from them and looked back with exasperation. "Plans?"

"Yes, Nicole, plans. Rehab. Treatment. What are your plans about your future in light of what just happened?" Her mom's voice betrayed the level of disappointment she felt about Nicole; at least, that's what Nicole heard.

"Mom, I don't have any plans, at least not yet. I'm not sure what you want from me."

"Want? I don't want anything from you, Nicole," her mom said, now just on the edge of anger. "We just don't want you going through this again, and it's obvious you need help. What kind of help do you intend to get?"

"I don't know, Mom. Geez! Can't you just leave me alone for two minutes!" With that, Nicole got up and stormed back up to her room. At that point she wasn't sure if she was even going to make it a week before running out of there as fast as she could.

Now it was one week later, and Nicole had waited rather impatiently for her mother to finally leave for her ladies' group at church. Once she was sure everyone was out of the house, Nicole had packed what few things she had with her, sent Adrian a quick text, and waited for him to text her back that he was down the block, ready to pick her up.

She was sitting in her old room, waiting for the text, and once again wondering why she was feeling a sense of remorse and even dread at leaving with Adrian. She knew she couldn't stay there, but did she really want to go back to the lifestyle that very recently almost killed her?

Just then, her phone buzzed. Adrian would be at the end of the street in five minutes. Going to auto pilot, Nicole picked up her bag and made her way out of her room. This was the way it had to be. She knew that she didn't belong in this family anymore. She had already burned too many bridges and caused too much pain. She needed to be with her real family, the people who wouldn't judge her. Adrian loved her. He'd said so on many occasions, and she believed him. She had to. What other option did she have?

She started walking down the street to where she knew Adrian was parked. She didn't know when she started running, but she was completely out of breath by the time she reached the Mustang. He was smiling as she slipped breathlessly into the passenger seat.

"Welcome home, Baby," he said seductively. "Welcome home."

The would-be orderly from Corner Mountain Hospital was watching from a distance again. He saw and he waited. This was the worst part, but he couldn't interfere. At least not yet.

05

CHAPTER FIVE

*K*atherine's clandestine exit from the Bible study social was semi-successful, though she knew that Marlene would call her. Her phone buzzed for the third time since leaving the church, and it was Marlene, for the third time. Katherine loved her friend, but sometimes she really just wanted Marlene to leave her be. She absolutely did not want to be at church right at that moment, and she certainly didn't want anything to do with this new study.

What had Susan called it? Mother Abraham? Yeah, that was it. Strange title, Katherine thought. But strange or not, she had no intention of reading it, not right now. Just the short description Susan had given was enough to assure Katherine that she was in no place to read something like that. Maybe later, but not now.

She stopped at the grocery store on her way home to pick up a few things. Tommy ate like a horse these days, and she couldn't seem to keep enough food in the house to maintain his sixteen-year-old appetite. He drank the last of the milk that morning, as well as eating the last bit of cereal. As she walked through the aisles of the store, Katherine's mind began to wander, as it usually did, to her daughter.

Where had she gone wrong as a mother? What should she have done that she hadn't done? Katherine's entire life had become more about Nicole's issues than anything else, and consequently, everything else in her life suffered.

She no longer went to church with any regularity. She wasn't sure when it happened, but somewhere along the way she had begun to lose faith that God was in this with her at all. If He was, wouldn't He have done something by now? His inactivity looked to Katherine an awful lot like inattention, which just sank her further into a sadness that had snuck up on her. Her marriage was suffering incredibly, and poor

Tommy was relegated to figuring out his own life within the confines of his room. No matter what Katherine did, she couldn't bring herself out of this incessant depression, this overwhelming feeling that she had to do something to help her daughter.

She'd spent countless hours in the past years searching for Nicole when she disappeared. She checked the hospitals at least two or three times a week, and she had even gotten to the point where she checked the morgue records, as well. She called Nicole's old friends, tried to find her new friends, and she even tried showing up in those seedier parts of town where she knew Nicole had been seen so that she could ambush her. Her phone was full of unanswered texts and voice mails made to her daughter, trying desperately to find the right words. Maybe if she inserted herself enough into the situation, something would spark in Nicole that she had made a mistake. Maybe something Katherine did or said would be the thing that put an end to this nightmare.

But nothing worked. Katherine couldn't understand her daughter's apparent lack of concern or care for what she was putting her family through. This just wasn't her daughter, and Katherine convinced herself that she had to keep trying, even if that meant she neglected her husband, her son, her friends, and even herself in the process.

Lost in thought, Katherine didn't realize she had checked out and was heading toward her car when her phone buzzed again. It was Marlene. She really ought to answer, if only to get her friend to stop ringing her.

"Hello, Marlene," Katherine said as she unloaded the couple of grocery bags she had into her SUV.

Marlene laughed. "I knew that if I just kept at it, you would answer eventually. I'm nothing if I'm not persistent."

Katherine got in the car and started it while smiling at her friend. "Yes, Marlene. 'Persistent' is the nice word one can use to describe you." Marlene laughed again, and Katherine continued, "What is it?"

"Just checking on you, that's all. You left in such a hurry and without saying good-bye to the others that I thought something must be up."

"Nothing's up, Marlene. I just wanted to go. I needed to get some stuff done, that's all." Katherine simply didn't want to talk about Nicole right now. She was so tired of talking and thinking and feeling, that she wanted to turn it all off for a while.

Undeterred, Marlene said, "I get that, Kate, but I think you're running in the wrong direction."

Here it comes, thought Katherine. Here comes the lecture.

"And before you shut me off, I'm not going to lecture you. I just need you to hear me say that I see you; I see your pain, and I want you to always remember that I'm here for you."

Katherine sighed. "Thanks, Marlene. I really do appreciate it. I just want to be alone right now, that's all."

"I get that, too. I absolutely do. Please just remember that I'm here, though, okay?"

"I know. You're a good friend, Marlene. I'll be alright. I promise."

"Okay. Just call if you need me. And by the way, I picked up the new Bible study book for you. You left without getting one."

Perfect! Katherine thought sarcastically. "That wasn't necessary, Marlene. I don't think I'm going to come to this study series. Too many other things going on." She was unable to keep that same sarcasm out of her voice when she answered.

"That's disappointing, but I guess I understand," Marlene answered. "But I still think you should read the book. It sounds really interesting and timely, if you know what I mean." Marlene paused and continued, "You know, Katherine, you're not the only one in our group dealing with wayward children."

That stung. The truth was that Katherine rarely thought of what her friends were going through in terms of their children. She was so caught up in her own struggles with Nicole that she didn't take time to think of them. As a matter of fact,

Marlene was dealing with her own son at the moment, as was Alison. Marianne's children were still young, but she was having a difficult time, too. Katherine felt a sharp pang of guilt when she heard Marlene's words.

"I know. I'm sorry, Marlene. I guess I've been pretty selfish lately, haven't I?"

"Not selfish, per se," Marlene answered. "Maybe just preoccupied with your own stuff. We all do that, but what you do in yours is shut everyone out, including God. Maybe this book has something to do with you, too, not just the rest of us. I'm looking forward to reading it, and I think you need to read it, as well."

Katherine could see that she wasn't going to win this one with Marlene. Her friend was determined to bring her that blasted book, so she gave in. Taking it didn't mean she had to read it. "Fine, bring it over. I should be home in a few."

"Good. I'll be by your house in about fifteen minutes. Love ya, girl." And Marlene hung up.

Katherine drove home quietly. She didn't even turn on the radio. Alone meant alone, and even the sound of voices over the airwaves made her feel worse. She needed to shut out the world, and she would be able to do that as soon as she got rid of Marlene.

***

It wasn't unusual for the house to be so quiet, even after Nicole had come home some three weeks earlier. After all, she spent the majority of her time in her room with the door shut. Without giving the quiet any thought, Katherine put the groceries away while straightening up the kitchen. She considered going up to check on Nicole, but she wanted to wait until Marlene had come. She knew it would only be a couple more minutes before her friend rang the doorbell, and Katherine didn't want to have to run back downstairs to answer it.

She was just putting the milk in the refrigerator when Marlene arrived at the door. She was holding a clear plastic bag in one hand and a Starbucks coffee in the other.

"Got you your favorite—a skinny vanilla latte with a sprinkle of cinnamon." Marlene held the paper cup out to Katherine.

Katherine smiled and accepted it while stepping aside so Marlene could come in. "You really are the best, Marlene," she said.

Marlene came in and headed for the dining room, placing the bag on the table. "I figured you could use a little pick-me-up. I know I needed one."

Katherine took a gratified sip and said, "Mmmm, just what the doctor ordered. Thanks."

Marlene was already sitting at the table, so Katherine sat down across from her, already trying to decide how best to abbreviate the conversation so that she could go back to commiserating alone. "Is this the book?" she asked, pointing to the bag Marlene had brought.

"Yep," Marlene answered. "I'm telling you, Kate, this book looks like it might be something special. I've never heard of the story of Sarah as it relates to Isaac and the time Abraham took him to use as a sacrifice, have you?"

Katherine shook her head and took another sip of coffee.

"Well," Marlene continued, "I'm looking forward to reading it. I'm not sure why, but I've got this feeling that we need these words right now." She looked Katherine in the eyes and said, "I think you need them right now, too."

Katherine only smiled wanly, not wanting to get into any kind of long dialogue about the book. She didn't want company, and taking Marlene's bait to discuss the book would negate any possibility of that happening.

Marlene got the hint. "Okay, I'm leaving," she began as she stood, but then she suddenly stopped and looked intently at Katherine again. "But promise me something. Promise me you'll read it. It's not too long, shouldn't take you much more than a couple of days to get through the whole thing. Just promise me you'll read it, okay, Kate?"

That wasn't fair, and Marlene knew it. Katherine's biggest pet peeve was broken promises. She often quoted the Bible passage that said we should all let our "Yes" be "Yes" and our "No" be "No." Katherine detested when people broke their promises. There had been far too many of those in the Matthis household of late, and she was determined not to add to that count. However, she didn't want to tell Marlene she wouldn't read the book because that was sure to incite a long conversation about why. On the other hand, she wasn't about to tell her that she would read it and then not do it.

"I'll read it. I promise," she finally said.

Marlene knew Katherine, and she knew that if Katherine said she was going to do something, come hell or high water, she was going to do it. "Good. That's all I ask," she finished as she made her way to the front door.

As soon as Marlene was safely out of the driveway, Katherine risked a look at the cover of the book left on her table. It looked pretty much like one would expect with a title like that. There was a woman dressed in ancient Middle Eastern garb, looking forlorn and distraught. However, it was the caption underneath the title that caught Elizabeth's attention. The title simply read:

Mother Abraham

But then the caption underneath read:

The story of every mother's struggle to let go

The words caused an involuntary shudder down Katherine's spine, mostly because this had been the subject of so many of hers and Ken's fights lately. He would tell her that she needed to let go of Nicole, and she would tell him how insensitive he was being. Generally, the fight would escalate to a point where Katherine made some terrible comment about how she loved their children more than he did, at which point Ken would storm out of the room. She knew she was being unfair, but to be truthful, she really did feel that she simply loved Nicole more than Ken did. Why else would he be able to let go so easily when it was impossible for her to even think it?

Now she was looking at the subtitle of a book that pointed out this struggle, but the thing that sent chills of anxiety down Katherine's back was the implication in the words. The subtitle seemed to imply that "letting go" was something that had to be done, and mothers everywhere struggled with it. This was a notion that Katherine simply couldn't fathom or entertain. It was her job to protect her children. It was her responsibility, had been her responsibility since they were born. If she let go, she'd be throwing them to the wolves. And Katherine would not do that. No way.

But still, the book intrigued her, if only just a little. She picked it up, tucked it under her arm, and headed upstairs. Nicole's door was closed, as usual, so she walked past it to her own room. She placed the book on her bedside table, fully expecting it to gather a fair amount of dust before she kept her promise to Marlene and actually read the thing. After laying the book down, she went back down the hall toward her daughter's room.

"Nicole?" she said through the door, knocking gently. "Are you asleep, honey?"

Nothing.

She knocked harder. "Nicole? Wake up; I need to talk to you about some things."

Still nothing, not even a creek of the old mattress on the hide-a-bed. Even when Nicole was trying to ignore her, the squeaks in that old mattress gave her away every time. But Katherine wasn't hearing anything.

"Nicole?" she yelled loudly this time. "Nicole, stop being a brat and open this door!" She jiggled the handle, fully expecting it to be locked, but it wasn't. The doorknob turned easily in her hand. She stepped tentatively into the room and immediately saw that it was empty. She looked around briefly, and quickly noticed that Nicole's big leather backpack that she took everywhere with her was not on her desk like it usually was. Katherine looked on the floor and all around, but she didn't see the backpack anywhere. She looked in Nicole's closet, and that's when the reality of the situation began to hit her. Nicole's clothes were gone.

She plopped down on the bed and didn't say a word. She didn't cry or get angry or anything. She just sat there, feeling numb and exhausted. Her daughter was gone again, and she wasn't sure she had the energy to start the cycle again. Every other time Nicole disappeared, Katherine began her diligent sweep of all the known places and people, trying every avenue she could think of to find her daughter. These misadventures always ended the same way, with her spent and in despair.

Katherine would then go home, where Ken never seemed to support her, at least not anymore. Sure, at first he was right there by her side, but the last few times he said he didn't see the point. He said that Nicole was an adult and that they needed to let her do whatever she was going to do. Katherine was indignant that he would even suggest such a thing! Leave her to do whatever she was going to do? What sense did that make? They had to find her, help her. They had to bring her home!

But this time Katherine didn't think she had it in her, and that scared her. Was her love for her daughter waning? Was there something wrong with her? Had she gotten that hard-hearted?

So, she sat on the edge of the bed, arms hanging loosely by her sides and staring straight ahead into nothingness. Part of her wanted the tears to come. That was a familiar place, because those tears always led to action. But none came. She just felt empty.

Eventually, she got up and walked out of the room. She wasn't sure how long she had sat there, but it felt like a long time. When she glanced at the clock on the wall in the living room, she saw that it had indeed been over an hour. Katherine knew what she was feeling, but this was a new level. She was sad, but this sadness was deeper than she ever remembered.

This was not how things were supposed to go.

She still remembered the day Nicole came into their world, kicking and screaming from the second her lungs breathed their first. Oh, how Katherine loved that baby! She was perfect in every way, and Katherine didn't think she could ever love anything more. Truly, she went into motherhood the way she did most things—with a vengeance, and there wasn't anything that little Nicole wanted for. Katherine made sure her life was complete, from the homemade baby food to the best crib money could buy. Ken used to tell her that she fussed over their new baby too much, but Katherine didn't care. She knew that her daughter depended on her for everything, and everything was what Katherine was going to give her.

Silently walking through the empty house now, Katherine thought that all of this just seemed wrong. This was not the way things were supposed to turn out. Once again, she turned to that nagging question—What had she done wrong?

At some point, she wandered into her own bedroom and lay down on the bed. All energy had left her, and the only thing she wanted to do was sleep. She closed her eyes, wanting to escape this sadness. Somewhere inside, Katherine knew she was tumbling toward complete despair, but she was lost as to how to stop the descent. Eventually, sweet sleep did come, but that sleep turned out to be anything but sweet. She dreamed. She dreamed of lost babies and neglected children. She dreamed of every mother's nightmare, and the tears finally came as she slept.

06

CHAPTER SIX

Katherine awoke with a start when she heard the front door slam shut. It was only a few seconds later when she heard her son calling for her.

"Mom! Are you here?"

"In my room," she answered, but she wasn't sure she had said it loudly enough for him to hear.

Tommy did hear, though, and he frowned immediately. He knew that tone in his mother's voice, and he usually heard it only when something bad had happened. Generally, that bad thing was about Nicole.

Before long, his handsome—but still boyish—face appeared in her doorway. He saw his mother lying on the bed, her forearm draped over her eyes, still wearing her shoes from this morning. No, things were not good.

He walked gingerly over to the side of the bed and sat near her feet. "Mom? What's the matter?"

She didn't answer at first. She just continued to lay there.

"Mom?" he asked again, this time laying his hand gently on her foot.

"She's gone again, honey," Katherine finally answered.

Tommy knew it before his mom said it, but he couldn't stop the anger. "Big surprise that is," he said sarcastically. He quickly got up from the bed and stormed out of his mother's room.

He was sick of this merry-go-round. He was sick of his sister always letting everybody down, and he was sick of watching his mom go through this each time she did. But more than anything else, Tommy was sick of being let down himself. He loved Nicole so much, and every time she disappeared, he felt like a little piece of him disappeared along with her.

They had always been close growing up. Nicole took care of him. She never made him feel like the unwanted little brother, even when her friends didn't want him around. Nicole never left him out. She always let him tag along with her and her friends, and he idolized her.

Tommy really couldn't pinpoint when it all went south with Nicole. To him it just seemed like one day she didn't act like his sister anymore. He knew from listening through the walls at his parents' "conversations" that they thought it started when she entered high school and was no longer the best at soccer. But Tommy thought differently. He noticed it long before then. He just didn't tell anyone.

It was gradual, but Nicole began getting really irritated when Tommy was around about a year before she started high school. She made some weird comments occasionally, like, "I'm not as perfect as you, Tommy, so why don't you shut up" or "Go back to your perfect little life, you little mamma's boy." He was confused by this shift, but he also didn't know how to respond to it. He just stopped hanging out with her as much. She would still let him come around sometimes, but those times became more and more infrequent. None of that meant that Tommy didn't want to be with his big sister. He just wanted her to want him around, and she mostly didn't.

Of course, after she started disappearing, which came a while after she found her new set of friends, Tommy noticed that there would be a brief period of time after she got home that things got better. Nicole was nicer and wanted to spend time with him. However, that was always very short-lived, since Nicole would disappear again within a couple of weeks. Tommy knew his mom kept hoping that each time was the last time. He did, too, but each time wasn't the last time. Each time just seemed to set them all up for disappointment the next time.

Well, Tommy was sick of it. He was sick of trying to believe that his sister had changed. He was sick of hearing his parents argue about her. He was sick of watching and waiting for the time when she came home, wondering if she actually would this time, and he was super sick of watching his mom go through this over and over again.

But the biggest thing Tommy was sick of was having hope. Even the notion of hope where Nicole was concerned was the worst disappointment of all, and he wasn't going to do it anymore. He was done.

He went to his bedroom, gathered up his baseball gear, and headed back out the front door. He determined not to think about his sister anymore that night. He had a game to play, and he intended to concentrate on that.

***

Katherine was vaguely aware of the sound of the front door opening and closing again, signaling the departure of her son. She knew she should be concerned for him, and certainly, part of her was. However, the sadness and despair she felt over this seemingly never-ending process of losing her daughter was too much to bear right then. She was sinking in it, she knew that, but she was helpless to stop the descent. She felt like she was in a spiral she couldn't find a way out of. She'd tried everything. She'd done everything she could think of, and yet, none of it worked. Saving her daughter was her job! Taking care of her, nurturing her, those were her responsibilities, but she wasn't doing that. This feeling of helplessness was inescapable, and it was horrible. There were no more tears, though. Katherine was officially cried out. Instead, she was losing herself in this pit of pain, and she couldn't see a way out of it.

Sometime later, Katherine heard the front door open and close again. She jumped up instinctively, running down the steps.

"Nicole? Nicole, is that you?" she called as she made her way to the front door.

She stopped short when she almost ran headlong into her husband.

"No, it's not Nicole. Why, where is she?" Ken asked after Katherine backed away in surprise. "I thought she was here."

Katherine didn't have the energy to answer. She slowly turned toward the kitchen and made her way in that direction. Ken followed right behind her.

"Kate, where is Nicole?" Ken asked again.

Katherine slumped at the dinette table in the kitchen, but still she couldn't muster the energy to answer her husband. Ken sat down across from her and waited for her to speak.

"Kate?" he tried again.

"How am I supposed to know where she is, Ken?" Katherine blurted out. "I came home from Bible study, and she was gone. Her clothes are gone, and her bag is gone, and she is gone. Okay?"

"Gone where?" Ken asked again, still trying himself to process what was going on.

Katherine looked up at him sharply, anger suddenly boiling to the surface, anger at Nicole, anger at God, and anger at Ken for not being in this with her, at least not to the extent that she felt she needed him to be.

Ken sat back instinctively, surprised by the sudden vehemence with which his wife looked at him. Things had been cold between them for a while now, but he thought he saw hatred in her eyes at that moment.

"I told you I don't know, Ken." Katherine was speaking through clenched teeth. "You don't care anyway, so what's the difference?" With that, Katherine got up from the table, almost knocking her chair over in the process, and stomped back up to their bedroom.

Ken just sat there, motionless at the table. He truly didn't understand what had been going on with his wife. At first, she and Ken put up a united front with Nicole. They stood together and worried together. However, in the last few years, Katherine became consumed with helping their daughter. Many times, Ken had tried to tell her that Nicole was an adult and had to make her own decisions. But each and every time he brought that up, they either had an all-out knock-down argument, or Katherine would simply stomp away.

Over time, these bouts became the norm when they discussed Nicole.

Eventually, they settled into a very uncomfortable existence, where they simply didn't discuss their daughter at all. For some reason, Katherine interpreted Ken's silence as a lack of care, but that was absolutely not the case. He didn't go off the deep end like Kate did, but that didn't mean he didn't care. He just wasn't weirdly consumed with it like she was. Truthfully, Ken didn't know what to do any more than Katherine did, but he also didn't know what to do with Katherine. Every time Nicole sank a little lower, Katherine went right along with her. Why couldn't she let go? Why was she hanging onto some notion that she could save their daughter?

Ken sat there, alone, for a little longer, and then he got up to make himself something to eat. He knew he'd eat alone again tonight, but that, too, had become the norm.

***

Alone again in her room, Katherine lay back down on the bed. She was so angry with her husband, but she had to concentrate to think of why. Of course, she knew at some level that she was really projecting her pain onto Ken, but she also knew that she genuinely felt that he didn't care for their children as much as she did. He never seemed to worry like she did. He never felt the need to go out and look for Nicole, ask questions about Nicole, or even mention Nicole with any frequency. It was almost like he adopted the notion of "Out of sight, out of mind" when it came to their daughter.

This infuriated Katherine, even though she knew Ken loved Nicole. She was most definitely the proverbial "daddy's girl," which made Ken's reaction to Nicole's lifestyle and frequent absences all the more puzzling. How was he able to dismiss the enormity of what was going on with their daughter so easily? Why was she so sad and he seemed so unaffected?

As Katherine thought about these things, her eyes wandered over to her nightstand. There, glaring at her from the corner of the stand, was that book. She stared at it, looking intently at the distressed woman on the cover. Mother Abraham.

Katherine still thought this was a nonsensical title, but despite herself, she couldn't help being a little curious. She reached over and took the book in her hands, flipping randomly through the pages. Marlene was right; it wasn't a long book. Actually, it was pretty short in comparison to some of the other books they had done in their weekly Bible study. There were only six chapters, and at the end of each chapter, there were a few "Thoughts for Consideration," along with one or two "Where are You?" questions.

She sat up, putting a couple of the pillows behind her head. Ken kept telling her she had too many pillows on the bed, but she didn't care. They were there as decoration, and she liked them. Besides, they afforded her extra neck support when she read in bed each night. She pulled the blankets up around her waist and opened the cover of the book. She had to do something to get her mind off of Nicole, and this silly book seemed like as good of a way as any. Before she knew it, Katherine was reading a story about a woman she thought she knew but was about to see in an entirely different light.

MOTHER ABRAHAM

CHAPTER SEVEN

- CHAPTER 1 -

Sarah said, "God has made laughter for me;

everyone who hears will laugh with me."

Genesis 21:6 (NASV)

$\mathcal{S}$he could smell the sweet aroma of bread wafting through the desert air as she laid out freshly woven pieces of wool on the stone. So often her work was impeded by dry, sandy wind, so she was fully taking advantage of the mild weather they enjoyed this day. She had earlier prepared a beautiful yellow liquid from a crop of pomegranates. She intended to use it to dye the woolen piece of cloth now laying before her. She had died another larger piece of fabric the day before from some myrtle they had gathered, and she knew the blending of its soft lavender with today's yellow would make a fine tunic for her son.

"No, no, no! Pay attention, my son! You must come to understand the sand so that you won't get lost in the desert," she heard her husband loudly proclaiming from across the camp. "We leave in only three days. These skills are vital to your survival."

Sarah looked up to see her husband bending over a series of mounds he had constructed in the sand at his feet. The two of them had been through so much together since they left Ur, and even though he was near 130 years in age, he was still agile and alert. His legs bent easily under his frame as he stooped over the mounds, using a small stick as his instruction tool on this particular morning. She loved him dearly, though at present, she was feeling more unsure of his plans than she had ever been in their time together as husband and wife.

"I'm sorry, Father. I fail to see how the sand drift can reveal direction," replied the young man stooping next to her husband.

Patient to the end, Abraham used the stick to point to one of the mounds on the ground. "You see, my son, the wind causes the sand to drift, and by observing the direction from which the drift moves, we can determine the direction we must go."

The young man looked puzzled.

"Look," Abraham began again, "do you see how the top of this mound leans in this way?" He pointed in the direction of the leaning point on top of the mound. "The horns of these mounds, like those on top of the great dunes in the desert, will point away from the prevailing wind, just as this one is now pointing away from where I was blowing on it a few minutes ago."

The young man looked on in earnest.

"Given that we know the wind at this time of year blows from the direction of the rising sun, or east," Abraham continued, "then we can know the direction that the horn is pointing is opposite to that, or west, the direction of the setting sun." He backed away for a second, allowing this to register in the young man's mind.

Suddenly, Abraham saw his son turn slowly toward him, a smile of recognition beginning to form across his face. "Ah, you see then?" Abraham smiled back.

"Yes, Father, I think I do." His son bent once again over the mound.

"When we know the direction of the prevailing winds, we can determine the other three directions from the horn of the crescent dunes in the desert, showing us north, south, east, and west."

Abraham clapped his son on the back, smiling back at him. "Excellent, my son, excellent!"

"Isaac," Sarah called. "Would you come here for a moment?"

Both men turned toward the sound of her voice. Isaac looked at his father for permission to leave their navigation lesson, and Abraham nodded with a smile. "My son, you will learn in time, after you have wedded yourself, that you never leave a woman waiting for you for any length of time." They stood together as Isaac smiled back at his father. "And that goes double if the woman is your mother."

Isaac laughed and turned toward the voice he loved with all of his heart. Sarah stood up from her task, a bowl of pomegranate yellow at her feet next to the long piece of wool she was about to dye. Isaac walked toward his mother with arms outstretched, embracing her the moment he got to her. This woman before him had given him everything she had. She loved him with all that she was, and she made sure he understood his value at every opportunity presented to her. Though older than most of the other mothers in the camp, she moved effortlessly throughout the sometimes harsh conditions in which they lived. She moved even more fluently within his heart.

Sarah settled into the arms of her son, arms that she once remembered as small and frail. Now, as he grew older, those same arms were strong and sure. He was now a man, though she would always see him as her little boy, her treasured answer to prayer. She wanted to hold him like this forever. She didn't want him to grow up, to grow away, to leave the safety of this home. Suddenly she heard the voice of her husband in her head, and she quickly pushed his words away.

"My son," she said softly, "my beautiful boy."

"Mother, I'm hardly a boy anymore." Isaac laughed into her gray hair, kissing her gently on top of her head. "I'm a man, and Father has been preparing me for a great quest, one toward which we must endeavor soon."

She knew, but she didn't want to think on that right then. Instead, she wanted to drink in the scent of her son, this promised heir that had stolen every corner of her heart.

After a few moments, Isaac said as he smiled, "Mother, are we to embrace until sunset, or did you call me to you for a specific purpose?"

Sarah's eyes popped open, and she realized she had been holding onto Isaac for much longer than was required to greet him. She let go quickly, raked her hands over her skirt as if to straighten it, and said, "Of course, my son. Forgive me. I simply needed to check the measurement of your chest before I finish your new tunic. I want it to be ready for you before you leave with your father." Even saying this made her stomach quiver, and once again, she pushed those feelings of dread aside.

Isaac began to laugh again. "It hasn't changed since yesterday when you measured it." But he moved obediently toward her again, this time with his arms held away from his sides.

"A good piece of clothing requires one to measure more than once, my son," she chided as she began to draw a string around his chest. "Don't presume that you know everything yet."

"Yes, beloved mother," he answered again, still smiling, though trying unsuccessfully to hide it behind his subjection.

Sarah couldn't help but smile back at him. Isaac could do no wrong as far as she was concerned. She couldn't bear for him to be hurt or mistreated in any way, and she certainly couldn't abide those who might do so. She'd seen to the banishment of that horrid servant and her son many years before. She had protected Isaac from everything within her power, often to the detriment of others, but that didn't necessarily concern Sarah. Her job was to protect him, to nurture and care for him. When the Lord had granted her such divine love as to give her a son in her old age, she had taken that job with all the gravity she felt it deserved. Isaac became her life, and she made sure no harm came to him from any direction.

"There," she said as she took the last measurement. "All finished. I believe it should be ready for you to wear when you and your father set out in a few days."

Isaac bent down to kiss his mother on the cheek once again. "You spoil me, Mother."

"Yes, well, that's my job, isn't it," Sarah answered with a smile. She patted him gently on the shoulder and said, "Now, you run along. I know for a fact that your father has much to tell you before you leave. There is also much preparation that still needs to be done."

"Yes, Mother," he answered as he turned to walk away. He stopped before he had turned completely and faced her once again. "I love you, Mother."

Her heart almost burst. Oh, how she loved this miraculous son. She could barely contain her love sometimes, and this was one of those times. "I know you do, my son, and I love you in return. Now run along," she answered him, though she was having a hard time not taking him in her arms for another long embrace.

Isaac smiled and bowed as he turned to leave, a little private joke between the two of them. Years before, when Isaac had learned that his mother's name meant "princess," he had started to bow before her on occasion, mostly just to have her chide him and tell him not to be so ridiculous. In truth, Isaac cherished the idea that YHWH Himself had given her such a name, and he overflowed with pride each and every time he thought of it. This time was no different, and it was also no different in that his mother threw a make-believe slap in his direction once he bowed in front of her. He was still giggling as he walked away.

Sarah stooped back over the stone on which lay the wool she was about to dye. She moved the fabric to another stone bowl and then slowly poured the yellow liquid over it. She used a polished stick to gently move the fabric around in the bowl, being sure that every part of it was immersed in the liquid. She would have to leave it to soak for half of the day, at which point she would dry it on another large rock. Hopefully, by the next morning she could begin sewing the two pieces together, artfully creating a beautiful lavender and yellow tunic for her beloved son to wear.

***

"But I do not understand, Abraham," Sarah was pleading as she laid the blankets out for them to bed for the night. "Why must you take Isaac to Mount Moriah with you? Why now? It is not the time for such communal sacrificing. I don't understand why he must go on your journey of personal obedience to YHWH. It is you who is to sacrifice, not Isaac. Our Father has directed you to go, not our son."

Ever since Abraham had told her that he was taking Isaac with him to offer a sacrifice to God, Sarah had had a bad feeling. Adding to it was her husband's strange mood ever since he'd returned from hearing from the Lord. Though she couldn't put her finger on it, Sarah knew something was wrong.

"Wife," Abraham answered sternly, "these things are as YHWH has directed. I do not question Him, and you will not do so either." With that, Sarah knew the discussion was over, but she couldn't turn away the fear that threatened to infiltrate her very being.

Abraham had returned from his morning prayers a few days earlier, but unlike when he generally returned from these sacred times, Abraham's countenance was downfallen. He spoke not one word the entire day, and after evening meal, he simply went to bed.

The next morning over first meal, Abraham announced that he was taking Isaac with him to Mount Moriah where the Lord had instructed him to offer a sacrifice. Certainly, it wasn't unlike Abraham to take their son with him when he went for ceremonial sacrifices, but this time seemed different. Her husband was sullen, contemplative even, and it seemed to Sarah as if he was embarking on something he almost dreaded. Since Abraham loved giving unto the Father of their bounty, Sarah's intuition began to sing. Something was very, very wrong, and she knew in the depth of her heart it involved her beloved Isaac.

"When will you leave?" she asked as she finished laying out the bedcovers. Sarah thought that maybe a few more distracting questions might entice her husband to reveal something more to her.

"We leave in three days' time," Abraham answered curtly. However, his demeanor quickly softened, and he turned to Sarah with new compassion in his eyes.

"My love," he began, "please forgive me." He moved toward her, placing his hands on her shoulders. The bond the two shared was strong, and the experiences they'd walked through as a couple had long since united them in just about every way imaginable.

He'd wronged her many times in the past as his faith faltered. He'd presented her as his sister to two kings on two separate occasions, both times to save himself. And though she was legally his half-sister, she was his entire wife. She would have been well within her rights not to forgive him such a trespass, especially since he'd done it twice.

Sarah had always been a beautiful woman, and he knew that the kings would each time hear of such a beauty coming into their kingdom. He'd told them she was his sister in fear of what they would do to him so that they could obtain his wife. They would do no harm to him as her brother, however. To his horror, each time the pagan king had indeed taken his Sarah into the king's harem, and each time, Sarah had remained silent.

It still burned Abraham's heart to think of his treasured wife in such a place, but his heart almost broke when he thought of how loyal she remained to him, of how she went to any lengths necessary to protect him, even when he had abandoned her for his own selfish reasons. Both times Abraham had gone to the king and told the truth. He simply couldn't allow Sarah's honor to be dashed just so that he could be safe. And both times, in His mercy, YHWH had come to his aid, influencing each pagan king to not only let them go, but to give them bountiful gifts to ensure they would leave.

The first time Abraham had done this, he thought she might never love him again, but of course, she did. The second time, however, he was sure he had lost her heart forever. Indeed, she was terribly wounded at his second betrayal of her, but as was her nature, she forgave him something that many women would have viewed as unforgiveable. Consequently, he vowed never to hurt her in such a way again. As a matter of fact, he endeavored to spend the rest of his life keeping her from any kind of pain whatsoever.

Yet here he was again, but this time under the direction of God. Abraham knew how much Sarah loved their son. Isaac was her world. She would do anything for their boy, and Abraham knew she would also die for him, if called upon to do so. How could he ever tell her the real reason he was taking Isaac with him to Mount Moriah? How could he tell her that the sacrifice was to be Isaac?

As he looked into her eyes, he saw there the young woman he'd left Ur with so many years before. Though much older now, she was still beautiful.

He couldn't tell her about Isaac. That much he knew. Instead, he needed to stall. "I'm sorry I have been so abrupt with you, my love. Perhaps I am just tired and in need of sleep." He put his hand over his mouth, stifling a yawn. "I'll lie down now, and we will speak of this tomorrow."

He kissed her lightly on the cheek and turned toward the palate of blankets she had made on the floor for them. He could feel her still looking at him as he laid down, but he turned over on his side and avoided her stare.

Sarah, gazing at the back of her husband lying on their bed, knew in her heart what Abraham was planning. Somehow her subconscious knew what the Lord had demanded of him, but she wouldn't allow herself to think of it. She couldn't. It was, after all, unthinkable.

She put out the lantern next to the bed, trying desperately to dispel the thoughts that were tumbling mercilessly around in her head. Her son's name was Isaac, which meant "he will laugh." Sarah had laughed when she'd heard the angel say she would become pregnant when she was already ninety years old and Abraham almost one hundred. Then she laughed again nine months later when she bore this wonderful child, but this laughter was for the unmitigated joy she felt at bearing a son.

She'd believed that the Lord instructed them to name their son "Isaac" to honor the joy this beautiful child would bring to them and to the world. He will laugh. Such a fitting name for the one who brought joy. How could it be that "he will laugh" might bring tears of sorrow instead of joy, tears of pain instead of peace. No, it couldn't be, so Sarah would not think it. She lay down next to her husband, who was already breathing deeply in sleep, and tried to think on anything other than what weighed her soul to its brink.

He will laugh. Yes, she will think on this.

He will laugh.

MOTHER ABRAHAM

08

CHAPTER EIGHT

Katherine laid the book back on her nightstand. She hadn't intended on reading the entire first chapter, but she got lost in the story. She'd gotten lost in Sarah's love for her son, something Katherine had never really contemplated before. However, it made perfect sense. This was Sarah's only son, the miraculous son born to a woman who had long since given up any hope of bearing a child for her husband. Katherine didn't know why she'd never really thought about how Sarah must have felt about Isaac, her miracle child, but it's not something anyone really talked about.

Katherine laid there on the bed for a while longer, thinking of a woman who lived thousands of years ago, but who shared in every mother's love for her children. What must it have been like for Sarah to know in her heart what her husband was going to do to their son? And how must she have been able to cope with these thoughts, knowing the origin of this horrible mission was God Himself?

Katherine couldn't fathom such a pain, and she found herself needing to stop thinking of it altogether. As she pondered Sarah, her own heart began to ache once again, and in her musings over the book, she'd almost forgotten why the pit in her stomach was there in the first place. But it only took a millisecond for the flood of pain over Nicole to resurface, and once again, Katherine was sinking.

Without really thinking much about what she was doing, Katherine reached for the book again. She needed to distract herself some more, avoid the pain of her own life a while longer. Then she remembered that there were a few questions or thoughts or something like that at the end of each chapter. She thumbed through the first pages of the book until she found the last part of chapter one. There she saw a couple of questions under the heading, "The Heart of Mother Abraham," and a couple of questions under "Your Mother Abraham Heart." It was one question in this last section that caught her eye.

What is your first reaction when you see that your children need you?
Why do you think you respond this way?

This question caught Katherine's eye because it's not what she expected to see. She expected to see something about love or devotion to God, or even devotion to one's spouse. But a question about what she was willing to do for her children when they were in need? That seemed almost nonsensical. What mother wasn't willing to do whatever their children needed? Wasn't that the definition of motherhood?

She didn't even see a need to answer it. Instead, she closed the book and rolled over onto her side. She knew she should go downstairs and talk to Ken or even eat a little something, but she just couldn't seem to get up the energy to do either. She also knew that she'd missed Tommy's game, but she didn't have the energy to think about that. She wanted to sleep. She wanted to forget and not feel what she was feeling, and what she was feeling was complete helplessness. She couldn't feel that anymore. She needed to escape, and sleep was the only way to do that.

In only a few moments, her clouded mind gave in to the darkness it craved, but with it, more dreams. Katherine dreamed of lost babies again, crying in the wilderness, and all of them somehow her responsibility. In the dream, she looked and looked for them, but they were always just out of reach.

Ken came in about an hour later and watched his wife moan, tossing and turning on the bed. Every once in a while, he thought he heard her say, "Nicole," and then something that sounded like "sacrifice," but he couldn't be certain. He went over and covered Katherine with the blanket that lay at the foot of their bed, watching in his own private pain of helplessness while his wife battled something he just couldn't understand.

***

The next few days were little more than a blur for Katherine, not because she was particularly busy, but because she just couldn't focus…on anything.

She'd had to deal with a very angry and hurt Tommy when no one showed up at his game. While she thought she had smoothed things over on the surface, she could tell that her son was still holding onto some hurt feelings. She didn't blame him. Katherine could only imagine how frustrating and lonely his last years had been when everyone in his family was so preoccupied with Nicole all of the time. Still, Tommy handled it like a champ. He never complained, and until recently, he never even seemed to be bothered that much. Katherine had a feeling, however, that things had been bothering her son more than he let on in the past. It looked like he was finished hiding it, and again, she couldn't blame him. It wasn't fair, but she was hard-pressed to know what to do about it.

Everything about the "Nicole situation" was all-consuming, at least for her. Katherine had put all other aspects of her life on the back burner since Nicole started going downhill. Unfortunately, that included her husband and son. Katherine recognized it but was unable to move outside of it. Nicole needed her, and she was determined to do all that she could to save her daughter.

She'd gotten up that morning, after what felt like a few days of going through the motions in life, and was absentmindedly wiping the kitchen counter when her cell phone rang.

Was it Nicole? The hospital? The morgue?

These thoughts raced through Katherine's mind in rapid fire succession as she ran into the living room where she last remembered seeing her phone.

By the time she got to it, her stomach was in knots, and she could barely make her fingers work well enough to press the green "Answer" button.

"Hello," she said anxiously, almost shouting into the phone.

"Why are you yelling?" It was Marlene. Katherine almost collapsed onto the floor with the release of all that emotion. "Did I interrupt something?" Marlene continued as Katherine slumped onto the couch trying to catch her breath.

"No, I'm sorry, Mar," Katherine finally answered. It took her a couple of seconds of measured breathing to make her heart calm down a bit. "I was just expecting another call."

Marlene sighed. "She's gone again, isn't she?"

Once again, Marlene proved why she was both Katherine's dearest and most exasperating friend. Absolutely nothing was lost on . But Katherine also knew that it was no use trying to lie to her friend either. Marlene would catch the lie just as quickly as she caught the tension in Katherine's voice.

"Yeah," Katherine relinquished. "She left a few days ago." She sighed herself and sat back on the couch. "I don't have the faintest idea of where she might be this time. But I'm sure she's with that awful Adrian."

"Did you go look for her?"

"No, not this time," Katherine answered. "I wanted to, but Ken convinced me I shouldn't." She frowned at the memory of that argument. She had agreed only on the promise that if Nicole didn't turn up within a week, she would go and look like she had in the past. She expected her husband to support her if that came to be the case.

"I'm surprised you listened to him," Marlene said. "Usually you do whatever you want when it comes to Nicole."

Katherine was pretty sure she didn't like the implication in Marlene's words, but she was too tired to argue with her friend, too. She decided to let the comment slide and change the subject. "What's up, Marlene?"

Marlene chuckled a little and answered, "Okay, I'll drop it…for now. Anyway, what I'm calling about is the weekly study. It's this morning, and I was hoping you had changed your mind and might come."

This morning?! It's been a week? Katherine was completely shocked that it was already time for the weekly study. How had she lost an entire week?

"You there?" Marlene asked after a few seconds of silence.

"Yeah. Sorry, Mar," Katherine answered as she tried to gather herself. "I really wasn't planning on attending this series. I told you that already."

"I know what you told me, Katherine, but I also think I know what you need, and that's not isolation. You need to be with your friends. You need to be with those of us who love you and can support you, especially in the church."

Katherine didn't answer.

"Did you at least start reading it?" Marlene asked when Katherine remained silent.

Katherine sighed. "Yes, as a matter of fact, I did."

"Well, wonders never cease," Marlene said sarcastically. Katherine rolled her eyes and waited for her friend to continue.

"Then you know how awesome it is, right?"

The book had been intriguing. Katherine would give her that. But awesome? She wasn't sure she was willing to give it an "awesome" at that point.

"I've read only the first chapter, but it's pretty good," Katherine conceded.

Marlene laughed again. Katherine wasn't sure if she was laughing at her or not, but she was pretty sure her friend was at least laughing at how difficult Katherine was being. That made Katherine smile, in spite of herself.

"Well, at least you're reading it," Marlene said. "Now, come to study with me. What can it hurt? The last thing you need right now is to sit in that big house alone."

Deep inside, Katherine knew that Marlene was right. She shouldn't be meandering around the house all day. She was close to driving herself crazy already. She knew she needed to get her mind off of Nicole, but she wasn't sure it should be by talking about this particular subject. But still, the book had piqued her curiosity a bit, and she had enjoyed reading the first chapter. Katherine knew that the other ladies would expect her to talk, but that didn't mean she had to. She could just go and listen. At least then she might not be thinking about Nicole for a little while.

"Alright, I'll go," Katherine finally said.

"You will?" Marlene exclaimed. "Wow. That was a whole heck of a lot easier than I expected it to be."

"Yeah, well maybe I just don't want to hear you beat me over the head for the next half hour with all of the reasons you think I should go."

Marlene laughed. "Smart girl. I had some good arguments all loaded and ready to shoot."

"I bet you did," Katherine said with a smile. "Can you come and get me? Ken took my car this morning while his is in the shop."

"Sure," Marlene answered. "Be there in an hour?"

"I'll be ready," Katherine said, and then quickly added, "And Marlene, thanks. For everything."

"I love you, girl," Marlene answered. "Be there soon."

Katherine hung up and sat silently for a few more minutes. She really didn't want to go. The last thing she wanted right then was to put on her nice face and try to have conversations with people. But again, she knew better than to try and cancel on Marlene now. That woman was coming in an hour, no matter what Katherine might text her between now and then. Yep, Marlene was exasperating, but Marlene also loved Katherine as no other friend ever had.

Katherine finally got up from the couch and made her way slowly up the stairs to her bedroom to get ready. As she passed Nicole's room, she paused and looked in mournfully.

Where are you, Baby Girl? Where are you?

Katherine stood there for only a few seconds before willing herself to continue on to her own room. She had never known a sorrow so profound before, and its depth came mostly from this feeling of utter helplessness. She was powerless to do anything to save her little girl.

God, she thought, please protect my baby. And please bring her home.

Katherine wiped away the single tear that had formed at her right eye and moved toward the nightstand where the book lay. She looked at the anguished woman on the cover and touched the woman's face gently. She looks about how I feel, Katherine thought again. She stroked the image of the woman's tear-stained face for a second more and then turned toward her closet. Marlene would be there soon, and Katherine needed to turn the pain off. At least for now.

***

On the other side of town, deep in the recesses of an old warehouse, Nicole lay shivering on an old mattress. She was barely conscious, but she was aware enough to know that she was cold, in pain, and alone. Just before she passed out again, she could have sworn she saw someone in the corner.

"Mom?" she croaked, "Is that you?" A rat scurried out of the corner, rocking a mannequin stored in the shadows. Nicole allowed a small whimper to escape her lips before unconsciousness took her again.

CHAPTER NINE

$\mathcal{C}$orner Mountain Community Church had been a place of sanctuary for Katherine in the past. As she and Ken navigated the mysteries of rearing two children, along with the obstacles that also came in their marriage, Katherine had found solace within the walls of this church. She could count on seeing Jesus on the faces of those she saw there, and no matter what was going on in her life, this was where she knew she could go to find comfort.

That was until this stuff with Nicole.

Transparency had never really been an issue for Katherine before the Nicole circus. She supposed in retrospect that was because nothing had really happened in her life that she was terribly embarrassed by. There were the odd problems with raising two children and maintaining a healthy marriage, but those were easy enough to talk about. But this stuff with Nicole was different. It just seemed like too much to share, and Katherine wasn't sure she trusted just anyone with this kind of family crisis. What if they judged Nicole? What if they judged her, or Ken, or their family?

No, Katherine had decided that Nicole's addiction issues were going to be reserved for a very select few people, and most of the people at her church were off that list. It wasn't anything personal. Almost everyone was off that list.

That's one of the reasons that Katherine was so reticent about attending this particular Bible study. Mother Abraham was coming close to stepping on all of Katherine's well-guarded toes when it came to mothering Nicole. Just reading the first chapter, though interesting, also made Katherine leery about sitting in a small group and discussing motherhood at this level. Something inside of her literally screamed "Stay away!" at the thought of both reading this book and attending a group of women who were going to discuss it.

Katherine was battling all of these feelings as she and Marlene pulled into the church parking lot. She almost asked Marlene to turn around and take her back home. She could make up a stomachache or a headache or some kind of ache. Anything to give her an excuse to make a hasty stage left exit from this charade.

However, Marlene got out of the car and started walking toward the side entrance of the church so quickly that Katherine had to almost run to keep up with her. Marlene acted like she knew that Katherine was going to try to get out of going in at the last minute. And of course, she was right on the money. Sometimes it was almost like Marlene was in Katherine's head, and she wanted her friend to get out of there! How was she supposed to manipulate situations if Marlene was always one step ahead of her?

"You running from a fire?" Katherine asked sarcastically as she caught up to Marlene in the foyer. Marlene never even turned to look at her but just kept walking down the side hall that led to the larger meeting room where the Bible study group met.

Katherine grimaced and began jogging along behind Marlene when it became evident that Marlene wasn't going to answer her. Before she could protest more, Katherine found herself walking through a doorway into a room full of eager, and loud, women.

They were headed for the round table at the far right of the room toward the back where she and her friends generally sat. Katherine could see Alison, Marianne, Kelly, and Beth already seated there, but also at the table were two faces that Katherine didn't recognize. One of the new women was animatedly talking with Marianne, while the other sat quietly, head bowed, seemingly finding something in her lap very interesting.

Beth saw Katherine first and exclaimed, "Oh, Katherine, I'm so glad you're here!" She got up to give her a hug as Katherine looked menacing at Marlene.

Marlene shrugged as if to say, "I don't know why she's acting that way," but Katherine glared still harder. Marlene must have told them something about what was going on with Nicole.

"We've all missed you, Kate," Beth was saying. "Marlene told us you weren't planning on doing this one with us, and well, you were gone so much for the last two that we were sad to hear that. But here you are!" She was hugging Katherine again, something Beth did a lot of.

"Yes, I'm here," Katherine said into Beth's neck when it became apparent that her friend wasn't letting go any time soon.

Suddenly the other three women were hugging her, too. Just one uncomfortable five-women hug. "We all missed you, Kate," Alison said after she joined in.

"Okay, you four, let her breathe, will you?" Marlene said, trying to break up what she knew was something Katherine was hating. Thankfully, Susan began then, bringing the first week of the study to order.

"Hello, everyone, and welcome to our first week in our study of Mother Abraham."

Katherine didn't hear much else that Susan said. She was lost in thought as she looked at the cover of her book again. What was this distraught mother thinking, crying as her long, black hair blew in the desert wind? Was she looking for her child, too?

Suddenly Katherine realized that the ladies at her table were all getting up from their seats.

"Come on, Kate, we're going into one of the other classrooms. It'll be more private," Marlene said as she gathered her own things.

As Katherine picked her things up from the table, the new woman who had been talking with Marianne was suddenly next to her talking just about as animatedly as she had been with Marianne.

"Hi, my name is Cristy. You're Kate, right?" she asked as she thrust her hand out in Katherine's direction.

"Katherine." In truth, Katherine never liked being called Kate. It just seemed to be where most people went with her name. However, she had always preferred the formal Katherine to Kate.

"Oh, sorry," Cristy said sheepishly. "I thought they were calling you Kate."

"They were," Katherine said, as she continued walking behind the other ladies on the way to the next classroom. "I just prefer Katherine, that's all." She was vaguely aware that she was being sort of rude to this newcomer. She didn't mean to be. She simply didn't feel much like socializing, and this bubbly new woman was taking more of her energy than she quite frankly had to spare at that moment.

"Oh, okay," Cristy said as she jogged to keep up with Katherine. "Then of course, I will call you Katherine." She smiled and never missed a beat until they got to the classroom.

"So, here we are, right smack in the middle of Columbus. I never thought I'd live in Ohio, but you never know where God is going to take you, do, you?"

Katherine had missed most of what Cristy had said on the way to the classroom. She was somewhat aware that the woman was talking, but her mind was once again on Nicole. She had such a feeling of dread, like she just knew something awful was going on with her daughter. She couldn't shake it, and with it came the surge of "I've got to do something" that always came along with it.

Because she was so lost in her own thoughts, she didn't notice the other newcomer until they started moving chairs around to form a circle. The woman walked in, head still bowed, as they were rearranging the room to fit their sharing time. She stood over in the corner, not making eye contact with anyone. They were all sitting before anyone noticed her still in the corner.

"Honey," Beth said with her arm out, "why don't you come sit by me." Leave it to Beth to reach out to her. That southern charm always came through.

The woman sheepishly walked over to the empty chair next to Beth and sat down, book clutched to her chest, head still bowed.

"Well, thank you all for being here," began Marlene. There wasn't really a leader of the group, per se, but Marlene always helped everyone along. She was a born leader, though Katherine always told her it was just that she was born the bossiest.

"It looks like everyone has the book," Marlene continued. "Have you all had a chance to at least read the first chapter?"

There were nods all around, save the silent woman who still hadn't looked up.

"Me, too," Marlene said, "though it was really hard for me not to keep on reading. It was really interesting, don't you think?"

More nods.

Katherine tried to pay attention to the discussion after that. Every once in a while, she would add a comment, just so that Marlene wouldn't bug her later about not taking part. Consequently, that meant she had to at least pay cursory attention to what everyone was saying. There were comments about what life must have been like living in the desert as a wife and mother, comments about how much Sarah must have loved her only son, Isaac, and there was even a brief discussion about how it might have been being married to Abraham, especially after he lied about her to two different kings. The women in the group spoke openly, even Cristy, though Katherine had a feeling that Cristy didn't have much trouble talking in any situation.

The silent woman, however, remained silent. Katherine caught her peeking over her book, still held tightly to her chest, and each time she was looking right at Katherine. As soon as Katherine would catch her, she looked back down immediately.

The woman's name was Bridget. She knew because Marlene had coaxed it out of her when they first sat down, but that was all this woman was willing to share. She didn't exactly look scared to Katherine; she looked more distrusting than scared. Now, there's a story behind all that would be what Marlene would say, and Katherine didn't doubt that there was. Unfortunately, Katherine was so wrapped up in her own thoughts that she didn't really give Bridget much of her attention.

"What do you think, Kate?" It was Alison. Apparently, they had been talking about something while Katherine daydreamed, but she had no idea what that something was.

"I'm sorry," Katherine stammered. "What do I think about what?"

"Number two under 'Your Mother Abraham Heart' in the book," Alison answered.

Katherine looked down at her book, which was thankfully opened to the right page at the end of the first chapter. There she saw the heading, "Your Mother Abraham Heart," and under it the question she now remembered:

-What is your first reaction when you see that your children need you? Why do you think you respond this way?

Katherine cleared her throat. "Oh, I thought that question was kind of dumb." When she looked around and saw seven confused faces, she continued. "I mean, isn't the essence of motherhood to respond when your children need you? Why even ask that?"

Marlene was the one to respond, and Katherine knew what she was going to say before she said it. "You've missed the point, Kate," she began. "The question isn't challenging the validity of responding to the needs of our children. It's simply asking us to examine our instincts where our children's needs are concerned."

She couldn't help it. Katherine felt defensive. "I don't think I've missed the point at all," she answered, and Marlene knew she'd hit a button in her friend. She sat back and waited for the inevitable torrent she knew was going to come from Katherine.

"I think our instincts define our motherhood," Katherine continued. "We respond because we are mothers. I'm not sure why that needs to be questioned."

"It's not our instincts that are in question." It was Marianne this time. "I think it's what comes of our instincts. What do we do in response to those instincts? I think that's what they want us to examine."

"I think you're right, Marianne." Beth this time. "And I think that is a necessity as Christian mothers."

"What do you mean?" Marlene asked. Katherine noticed that Bridget looked up from the floor, even if it was only a bit.

"Well," Beth continued, "maybe there's an unhealthy aspect of mothering. Maybe without leaning on the Holy Spirit, our flesh might take mothering our children to an unhealthy extreme."

Katherine bristled. She didn't like the direction this discussion was taking.

Marlene noticed Katherine's distaste in their points, so she deflected. "You don't have to answer the question, Kate. It's probably best to contemplate the answer in our time, don't you think, ladies?"

"I don't mind sharing my answer," Beth interjected. "My instinct is to do everything for him. I have a hard time watching him fall down or get his little feelings hurt. But sometimes it's just my impatience that gets in the way. I mean, waiting on Alex to tie his blasted shoes in the morning drives me insane!"

They all laughed, all except Katherine and Bridget. Katherine stole a glance at the silent woman and caught Bridget looking at her again. Once again, she looked down the instant Katherine caught her.

"Half the time I just tie them myself so that I can get him to school before lunch!"

More laughter and comments of agreement.

Katherine could feel Bridget looking at her again.

"But mostly," Beth continued, "my instincts are to be everything he needs, to do everything for him so that he is safe and happy." She looked around the room. "Is that wrong?"

"No, I don't think so," Alison answered her. "I think every mother's instinct is to do everything for her children."

"I agree," Marianne added, "but is doing everything for them always right?"

They all looked down, and no one said anything. Katherine hadn't really ever thought of mothering from that perspective. When was everything too much? Where do we draw that line?

"Well, I think that's as good a place as any to stop for this week," Marlene said as she closed her book. "Let's try for two more chapters this week. The study is abbreviated to only four weeks this session, and I want to be sure we get through the entire book. Beth, can you pray us out of here?"

"Sure," Beth answered and began to pray. "Father, help us as we read this book to discern Your wisdom as we move in our motherhood. Guide us and bring us to a deeper understanding of mothering in Your grace. In Jesus' name we pray. Amen."

Everyone began moving then, picking up her stuff and replacing her chair to where she had gotten it. The church used these classrooms for Sunday school on the weekends, so they had to be sure to leave the rooms the way they found them. This classroom was one of the adult classes, so the chairs were regular sized. They'd had to meet in one of the children's classrooms from time to time, and those tiny little chairs were a challenge to get comfortable in, to be sure.

Katherine replaced her chair around one of the rectangular tables and turned to try and catch Bridget before she left. She was too late, however. Bridget had slid out almost as unobtrusively as she had slid in. Katherine decided that Bridget wanted to talk to others even less than she did. Part of her was curious about that, but once again, she was so consumed with her own worries that thinking of another person and her problems was pretty much out of the question.

She and Marlene rode in relative silence back to Katherine's house. Marlene thought about questioning Katherine on some of the things she'd said but thought better of it. She did know her friend quite well, and she knew that backing Katherine into a corner was never a good idea. Instead, Marlene decided to ask Katherine about something else.

"So, what did you think of the new ladies?"

Katherine shrugged. "Well, that Cristy is sure a talker," she answered, and Marlene giggled. "But Bridget makes up for her with all that silence. What's her story, anyway?"

"I'm not sure," Marlene said uncertainly. "Susan asked me specifically if Bridget could be in our group. Not sure why, and Susan didn't tell me anything about her. She just said that she thought Bridget would be a good fit."

"I'm pretty sure she could fit anywhere or even nowhere. I don't know if we will know anything about her in the short amount of time this study is going to take. She is shut as tight as a drum." Katherine thought again of how even Bridget's body language told others to stay away.

"Maybe it will be better next week," Marlene said as they pulled into Katherine's driveway. "She looked at you a lot," she added.

Nothing got by Marlene. "Really? I hadn't noticed," Katherine lied.

"Sure you didn't," Marlene said through a smile as Katherine got out. "Talk to you later?"

"Yeah, I'll call you. Thanks for the ride."

"Love you, Kate," Marlene said, but the car door was already shut. Katherine was really trying to shut her out this time, but Marlene wasn't about to give up. Instead, she prayed as she drove out of the driveway. She prayed that God would soften her friend's heart to hear Him in all of this. She prayed that whatever purpose God had for Bridget and for Katherine would come to pass, and she prayed for the safety of their children.

As she drove away, she prayed also that God would protect Katherine from Katherine.

***

Another day came and went for Katherine following Bible study. She knew she missed another of Tommy's games, but she just couldn't bring herself to go. The depression she was feeling was getting deeper and deeper, and she was falling faster than she ever had. Every moment was filled with thoughts of Nicole, where she might be and what she might be doing. She also couldn't shake the feeling that she should be doing something—anything—to help, but nothing came to her. Instead, she just felt stuck in immobility, and there she also felt failure and more sadness.

Ken came home later that evening and tried to have a normal conversation with her, but he finally gave up after getting little more than nods and grunts. Katherine couldn't stop the feelings of resentment she was having toward him either. He seemed so unconcerned for their daughter. He didn't even bring Nicole up. It felt like he didn't care at all.

Katherine went on up to their room early, breaking the uncomfortable silence they shared in front of the television. She wasn't sleepy yet, but she thought she might read a little to help her fall asleep. As she curled up in bed and brought the comforter up around her waist, she reached over to the nightstand and picked up the book again. Part of her didn't want to read any more, but another part was really curious about how Sarah was going to handle letting Isaac go with Abraham. Truthfully, Katherine wasn't making any connections to her present situation with Nicole, but she was connecting with Sarah as a mother. Besides, getting lost for a little while in someone else's drama seemed like the exact thing she needed right then. She flipped through the pages until she landed on the second chapter. She knew sleep was still a ways away for her, so she relinquished herself to reading until sleep found her.

"The next two days for Sarah were some of the most painful she had ever remembered…"

10

MOTHER ABRAHAM

CHAPTER TEN

- CHAPTER 2 -

And God said to Abraham, "I will bless her [Sarah], and give you a son from her!
Yes, I will bless her richly, and she will become the mother of many nations.
Kings of nations will be among her descendants."
Genesis 17:16 (NLT)

The next two days for Sarah were some of the most painful she had ever remembered. She tried desperately to hide her misery from her husband and son, but both knew her too well. They could see her misery, and though Isaac had no idea what plagued his mother, Abraham knew. Though neither had spoken of her fears, Abraham knew his wife was an intelligent woman, and she would have put facts together to surmise what this journey meant for their little family. Words were unnecessary in order for him to deduce the object of his wife's dread.

Therefore, they never spoke of those fears out loud. That was, at least, until the morning he and Isaac were to set off for Mount Moriah.

Sarah awoke with a pain in her stomach that she was ill at ease to identify, for in identifying the cause of the pain, she would also be forced to acknowledge its source. Somehow that acknowledgement seemed as if it would make her fears all too real. Consequently, she found herself mindlessly trying to go about her morning work, preparing the morning meal and directing her servants on the many tasks for the day. One of the tasks required food preparation for her family's trip that day, along with the two young men Abraham was taking with him.

Sarah found herself reminiscing about the promise YHWH had made to Abraham concerning their son and what his birth would signify. The promise had seemed too great to be real, and yet the son had been born just as the angels told her husband he would be. Surely, they must also believe the promises the Lord made in regard to their miraculous boy.

Sarah came to easily believe the promises God made in relation to Abraham. God had promised her husband many years earlier that He would make a great nation from her husband. The Lord said that Abraham's descendants would exceed those of the grains of sand one could find on the seashore. And of course, YHWH could do that, but she became convinced that this miracle could not come from her barren womb. That's when she devised the plan of using her servant, Hagar, as a surrogate mother. After all, the custom was well-regarded for those women who could not bear children themselves to have one of their servants do so for them. That plan had ended terribly as Hagar haughtily paraded her swollen body before Sarah, making her feel fully inadequate at the thought that she could not do for Abraham what this servant girl had so easily done.

Sarah still cringed at the memory of Hagar's behavior, sending her servant away while she was still pregnant. The Lord appeared to Hagar in the desert and told her to return, and though Sarah wasn't happy to see the servant again, she knew that sending her away was wrong. She knew that in her flesh she had tried to make a way where YHWH had already traveled.

It was at this point that the Lord spoke to Abraham again, but this time He reiterated His promise not only as it concerned Abraham, but this time He included Sarah in the promise. God promised that she would bear a son, and that in this birth, Sarah would be blessed. It would be through this son, her beloved Isaac, that nations would come and that kings would reign. And all of this would come from her womb. What a magnificent promise!

How could her suspicions be correct now? If YHWH had promised that nations would come from Isaac, who came from her, then she must be mistaken in what she suspected might come of this fateful trip to Mount Moriah. She wasn't sure how to bring her suspicions up to Abraham, and this is where her thoughts were gathered when she heard that beloved voice behind her.

"Good morning, Mother."

She stopped milling the grain on the stone in front of her and smiled in spite of her misgivings. Just the sound of his voice brought her unmitigated joy.

Sarah turned to face her son, now handsomely clad in his new lavender and golden tunic. She grinned and clapped her hands together in satisfaction. "Oh, my son, you are as beautiful as the sunset after a rain." She placed her hands on his arms and continued, "I don't think I've ever made you a finer tunic. The lavender is a perfect match to your eyes."

Isaac grinned and looked down sheepishly. "You embarrass me, Mother. You do remember that I am a man and not a woman, correct?" he said playfully.

Once again she slapped lovingly at his arm. "Of course I know that you are a man! You remind me daily that you are not a child. I suppose I at least perceive that you are a man. Can a mother not compliment her son when he wears a new garment?"

"Surely, you can, Mother. Sometimes, however, I would like to hear you use words fit for a man, and not those for a woman." He was smiling again, gently poking fun at Sarah.

They were used to this kind of banter between the two of them. Isaac had definitely learned his sense of humor from Sarah. His father was most often very serious, instructing Isaac daily on the Law and the many skills he would need to survive in the desert. Sarah, on the other hand, played with Isaac as a child, teaching him the fine art of hide-and-seek, and then as he got older, how to enjoy a good dose of word play when appropriate.

"Well, my son, maybe if you learned to run more like a man, I could do that," Sarah said quickly as she ran off into the camp. At her age, she shouldn't have been able to run as well as she did, and certainly, Isaac had no trouble keeping up with her. But he pretended to have a hard time catching her as she dodged here and there among the servants, knocking over a pot or two in her wake to slow him down.

"Unfair, Mother," Isaac yelled as he tripped and fell over the last one.

At the sound of his fall, Sarah stopped running immediately. All frivolity gone from her face, she ran back to her son as quickly as she could.

"Are you alright, Isaac?" she asked breathlessly, trying to help him back to his feet. "Is anything broken?"

Isaac stood up unaided by Sarah and said, "I'm fine, Mother. I'm fine." He was wiping the sand off of his trousers while Sarah tried to help him with that, too.

"Mother," Isaac said as he grabbed her hands, "please stop. I'm fine. You fuss over me too much."

Sarah looked into his eyes, and she melted again with love for him. She laughed and dropped her hands. "I'm sorry, my son. Old habits."

Just then Abraham appeared over the hill. He had been busy all morning preparing for their journey. They were set to leave in only minutes. Sarah had been trying every way she could think of not to think of it at all.

"Isaac!" Abraham yelled. "Where have you been? There is much to do! Come!"

Isaac lifted his mother's hands to his lips and kissed them. "I must go, Mother. See you at the caravan?"

"Yes, I'll be there," she managed to say, knowing that the tears were lurking just behind her eyes. She watched him run toward the caravan just as she also watched her husband approach.

"Is everything ready, my wife?"

Suddenly, and without reason, Sarah felt hot anger well up inside of her toward Abraham. The anger was not unexpected in its presence, as she had been dealing with hints of irritation with him for days, but it was unexpected in its intensity. She suddenly felt furious.

"Yes, everything is just as you instructed," she answered curtly, looking down to retrieve a few dates that had fallen from a cart she inadvertently bumped into while running from Isaac. Placing them back in the cart, she turned to leave, but Abraham stopped her.

He reached out to touch her arm, but she drew back. He straightened and asked, "What is ailing you, wife? Why are you angry?"

"I am not angry, husband," she lied. She knew she was angry, but she wasn't sure why. She only knew that she was angry with Abraham, really, really angry, and she didn't want to talk to him.

Abraham, knowing Sarah well, also knew better than to either believe her or to challenge her in this unbelief right at that moment. She would talk to him when she was ready, though he was fairly certain from where her anger stemmed. He didn't actually want to talk about that either.

Sarah continued to walk away when Abraham dropped his hand from her arm, but then she suddenly stopped. With her back still turned, she asked, "Who are you taking with you?"

"Micah and Hiram."

"And do they know where they are going?"

"They know all that they need to know." Abraham knew that Sarah was evading what she really wanted to ask, but he was loath to prompt her. He wasn't sure how he would answer.

Her shoulders slumped, and Abraham's heart broke for his wife. Yes, she was a wise and knowing woman, so chances were good that she had surmised what this fateful trip entailed. Would she trust him? Would she trust YHWH?

Suddenly she turned to face him, tears falling unimpeded down her cheeks. Abraham had to catch his breath as his heart broke even further to see his Sarah in such anguish. He knew she was fighting to honor him in this, to remain faithful. Sarah had always been an outspoken woman, but her outspokenness had occasionally led Abraham to making unwise decisions. He could not be dissuaded now.

"I need you to hear me, Abraham," she said, the gravity of brokenness on her lips. "If any harm comes to my son, I know not what will become of me."

"Why do you say such things, wife?" he asked, though he knew full well why she was asking.

She took a step closer to him. "Because that boy is my life. YHWH gave him to me, and he is mine, mine to care for and mine to protect. He is my answered promise, and if that promise is taken from me, I know not what I will do."

Abraham closed the distance between him and Sarah, gently taking her in his arms. She resisted at first, but then quickly relinquished. He held her there a moment, stroking the locks of her hair, kissing the top of her head before he spoke.

"My dearest Sarah, YHWH calls all of His children to obedience. He calls us to move toward Him in that obedience, but it is a call. There is a call on my life, there is a call on your life, and there is a call on Isaac's life. But there are truly many kinds of calls on our lives, and I believe there is one also on you as a mother."

He lifted her chin to look into his eyes as he spoke again. "Wife, this is not easy, but I pray you hear YHWH as He speaks to you. Often our calling requires that we deny something we think is right. Trust our Lord. He is good and He is loving, even when we don't understand." He kissed her on the forehead once more and turned toward the direction in which he had sent Isaac a few minutes earlier.

Sarah knew these words should comfort her, but they were hollow against the pain she was feeling. Still she didn't know exactly what Abraham was planning, exactly what the Lord had required of him concerning Isaac, but her insides told her it was horrible.

Would the same God who gifted her with this son also take him from her? She couldn't imagine a loving Lord doing such a thing. And why was Abraham so easily in obedience to such a horrendous act? She could feel the anger toward her husband welling up once again inside of her heart. Surely, she must love their son more than her husband did. Surely, her love was deeper, her pain more profound in that her reaction to the possibility of losing him was so much more pronounced than that of Abraham.

She watched as Abraham crested the furthest sand dune where she knew the small caravan was preparing to leave. She hurried off to their tent to be sure that all of the provisions had been loaded as she had specified.

As she walked hurriedly toward the tent, she was overwhelmed with despair she hardly knew possible. How could she let this happen? There had to be something she could do.

Her mind was still spinning with possibilities when she crested that same dune only minutes later, unsure of what might happen when she got there.

11

CHAPTER ELEVEN

Katherine was torn about continuing on in the book. However, Ken was still downstairs, and she wasn't really that sleepy yet. She turned the page and thought that one more chapter wouldn't kill her. She was beginning to really like Sarah, anyway.

12

MOTHER ABRAHAM

CHAPTER TWELVE

MOTHER ABRAHAM

- CHAPTER 3 -

God said, "Take your son, your only son, Isaac, whom you love,
and go to the land of Moriah, and offer him there as a burnt offering
on one of the mountains of which I shall tell you.
Genesis 22:2 (ESV)

*I*saac was busy loading the last of their provisions when Sarah crested the dune. He was such a handsome man. Sarah had caught many of the young women in their caravan looking at him, giggling with one another as if they were seeing something sweet they wanted badly. Sarah had no doubt that finding her son an appropriate mate would be no problem. However, he hadn't been in any hurry. For this, too, Isaac was the perfect son. He waited on the leading from his parents before he made any move to wed. He trusted their judgment, and he refused to consider such an important decision without their guidance.

She was almost half the distance from him when he looked up and saw her approaching. "Mother!" he cried with enthusiasm. "I was beginning to worry that you weren't going to make it to see us off." He ran to her and hugged her in that way he had that made her feel like she was the most treasured person in his life.

"Ah, you silly boy," she chided through a smile. "I would never miss saying good-bye to my favorite son."

It always pained Isaac a little when his mother said this. He remembered his half-brother, Ishmael, often, and just as often, his heart ached for the way both Ishmael and his mother, Hagar, had been sent away. Isaac understood why his mother did the things that she did when it came to him. He understood that her love for him often transcended both common sense and common courtesy. Still, he always felt badly about it.

"Come, Isaac." It was his father. "It is time to go."

Sarah didn't want to let go. She held on tighter.

"Mother," Isaac said through a smile, "why are you so distraught? Father says we will only be gone a few days." He lifted her face to his and kissed her lightly on her weathered cheek. When he looked in her eyes, however, he saw fear there. Isaac wasn't used to seeing this particular emotion behind the eyes of his strong mother. "What is it?" he asked.

Sarah thought briefly about asking him, begging him, if need be, to stay. She still couldn't put her hand on the reason why she felt so much panic, but she knew instinctively that something was different about this journey. Sarah's heart felt the pain of loss for her son, and that pain, though inexplicable, was very real. But looking now into the face of this gift that was her son, she also knew instinctively that she couldn't compromise her son's destiny with her fears. This would be neither wise nor kind.

"It's nothing, my son," she finally answered, looking down quickly so that her astute son could no longer read her heart through the doorway of her eyes. "Just an old woman letting her imagination run away with her." She smiled up at him briefly, careful not to hold his gaze for longer than a couple of seconds, and then she looked down again, moving away from him. "Now, go, my Isaac. Go with your father and mind that you take care of him. He's an old man, you know."

"Old?" Abraham had walked up behind her without her knowing it and heard her last comment. "Who says I am old?"

She turned to him and gestured at his body. "Every wrinkle and crevice I behold daily tells me, that's who."

He smiled and said to Isaac, "Micah requires your help, my son. Go now."

Isaac turned dutifully away, but not before kissing his mother one more time. "I love you, Mother, to the stars and back to the earth. I will always love you." And then he was gone.

Sarah could feel her breath catch as her son turned to leave. She watched him as he walked toward the caravan, concentrating on every breath she took so that she would remember to breathe. Why does my heart break so? she wondered silently.

"Sarah," Abraham said, breaking her concentration on Isaac, "it is time."

He reached out to her, but she drew back from his touch. Sarah knew she was behaving irrationally, but she couldn't help it. She was angry with Abraham. She was angry with God. She wasn't even sure what she was angry about, but her heart told her that something was going to happen to her son, and that something was something between her husband and his God. Much of her anger was at not being told, but more of her anger was at Abraham's apparent willingness to do whatever the Father was asking of him. Was there no limit to what he would do for YHWH, even at the expense of his one and only heir?

Abraham let his hand drop slowly. He couldn't tell her; of that he was most certain. He couldn't tell her how his own heart was breaking at this recent command from the Lord. He was confused and tormented over what he was going to be required to do, but for the first time in their marriage,

Abraham couldn't share his feelings with his wife. This was a foreign feeling for him, one of aloneness in these kinds of decisions, but at the same time, he knew this knowledge was not for Sarah. At least it wasn't for him to tell her. If YHWH wanted her to know, then YHWH would be sure she did. Besides that, Abraham was powerless to do anything at this point but leave his angry wife and do the bidding of his God.

Sarah watched him walk away toward the caravan. So much of her wanted to scream at him, make him tell her what he was planning to do, make him stay, make him at least seem to care! But Sarah also knew that what transpired next was completely out of her hands. Perhaps that was where most of her consternation and anxiety came from. She could do nothing. She couldn't protect Isaac, she couldn't rescue him, and she couldn't stop Abraham from doing whatever he was planning to do. She simply had to stand there and watch as they disappeared into the desert. Truly, she thought she might go mad in those next moments. How could she be required to do nothing? How could she be required to stand aside and allow possible harm to befall her only son, her gift from above? How?

Slowly she turned back toward the camp, wondering at how she was going to survive the next few days. There wasn't enough to work to do to keep her mind off of the impending doom she simply knew was about to come to Isaac.

She thought about making up a reason to follow them, making up whatever fabrication necessary so that she could intercept the caravan and bring her Isaac back home with her. What could she say? What lie could she use that would be believable enough to cause Abraham to allow their son to return with her?

She knew that no such lie existed, and her heart sank even further. In those moments, Sarah became convinced that this burden was simply too much for her to bear. She wasn't going to make it this time. She'd left her home and all that she knew to follow her new husband. She had borne the burden of Abraham's weakness and fear, finding herself twice in the harems of foreign kings. She had been the brunt of persecution and ill treatment from her horrible maid, Hagar, when Ishmael had been born. Then she had borne the same affronts on behalf of her son after Hagar and Ishmael were allowed back into the camp, watching the would-be-heir, Ishmael, tease Isaac and mistreat him.

She'd managed to take care of every situation in every instance so that she and her son were safe. She'd protected Isaac at every turn, even when Abraham was oblivious to the threats around his son. She had done that! Sarah had protected Isaac, nurtured him, cared for him, and loved him as no other mother in history had ever loved a son. How could she now do nothing for him, especially when the stakes seemed higher than ever? Wasn't it her role to do all that she could for her son?

Sarah walked gloomily into her tent, looking around aimlessly for something, anything to take her mind off of her pain, but there was no escaping it. She briefly thought she might go mad with the anguish of this limbo of activity. Everything in her screamed for action, and yet, there was nothing that could be done. Sarah was stuck, and Sarah was angry.

"Mistress?" came a voice from the opening to the tent. "There are traders here who wish to see the cloth we have for barter. Shall I gather it up and meet you at the center of camp?"

Sarah turned to see Talitha, one of her maid servants, standing tentatively in the entrance. Sarah had been so lost in her own misery that it took her a few moments to register what the young woman was asking of her.

Finally, she answered, "Yes, Talitha. I shall be there shortly."

"Very good, Mistress," the girl said and quickly backed out of the tent.

Sarah thought briefly about curling up on the blankets on the floor. Suddenly, sleep was the most attractive thing she could imagine. But there was work to be done, and she also knew that without her, much of this work would go undone. With legs that felt like rain-drenched sand, Sarah made her way out into the open court at the center of camp, barely able to keep the tears at bay.

How was she going to endure this, this sentence of nothingness? She didn't know, but the acute pain in her heart made her believe that she would not.

13

CHAPTER THIRTEEN

*K*atherine could feel the ache in her own heart as she finished reading this last chapter. As much as she hated to admit it, and most likely would never do so to Marlene, she really was identifying with this book. She had no problem picturing Sarah in those moments of her life when she had to let Isaac go. She knew the pain that poor woman must have been feeling at the helplessness in protecting her son. It is every mother's purpose to protect her children. How in the world are they then expected to ignore all of that and let them go off and possibly get hurt, or even die?

While she lay there on her bed, the book draped across her chest, she heard Tommy come home. She'd missed another game. Katherine knew that she was hurting her son each time she didn't show up. To make matters worse, Tommy had even stopped reminding her about the games. The poor boy had given up on a family that supported him. Katherine knew that she should go in and talk to him, apologize for not being there again. She just couldn't muster up the energy, though. It felt as if she had nothing left to give anyone. She'd lost herself in this despair, and she wondered how Sarah was going to deal with it.

Suddenly, her cell phone rang. She jumped and snatched it off of the nightstand as quickly as she could. She resisted the urge to scream her daughter's name into it, hoping even as she said, "Hello," that it was Nicole.

"Hi, Katherine. It's Marlene. Did I interrupt something?"

Katherine sighed audibly into the phone, unable and unwilling to hide the disappointment she was feeling that it was not Nicole on the other end. "No, Marlene, I was just reading."

"I hope you were reading our book."

"As a matter of fact, I was."

"I'm glad to hear that. But that's not why I was calling. First, have you heard anything from Nicole?"

Katherine sighed again and answered, "No, nothing. Of course, we almost never hear anything this early in the game."

"Still," Marlene said, "it can't be easy to wait. I'm so sorry, Kate. I really do wish there were something I could do."

"Believe me," Katherine said, "if there isn't anything I can do, there certainly isn't anything anyone else can do."

"Well, that's not entirely true, Katherine."

Katherine was getting irritated. "How is that not true? I'm her mother. If there were something anyone could do, it would be mine to do first, don't you think?"

It was Marlene's turn to sigh. "Never mind, Kate. I didn't call to argue with you."

"Then why did you call?" Katherine knew she shouldn't be so short with her friend, but she couldn't seem to help it. She was getting tired of having no one sympathize with her plight.

"I called to ask you to pray for Darren."

Just as quickly as Katherine's temper had flared, it was extinguished at the mention of Marlene's son. Guilt suddenly raged in Katherine's heart. She had not one time asked Marlene about Darren since Nicole had disappeared, and she knew better than anyone how broken Marlene was about her eldest son.

Darren had Down syndrome. He was twenty-nine years old, but he had the mental capacity of an eight-year-old. He still lived with Marlene and her husband, but they were slowly trying to help him move into some independence. The truth was that Darren had been a challenge of late. Whereas his mind was prepubescent, his body was definitely that of a twenty-nine-year old man. Because of that, he dealt with all of the needs that physical body had, including a need for companionship.

Darren had met a young lady at his job as a greeter at the local Walmart. She, too, had Down syndrome, and the two had quickly become friends. According to Marlene, however, their friendship too quickly escalated to a deeper attraction, one for which her son was ill prepared. This caused a lot of friction in the Turner household. Darren didn't understand why Marlene was trying to keep him from moving into this relationship, and Marlene was struggling with when to hold on and when to let go.

One day when Marlene had returned from the mall, she found that Darren was gone. He'd packed a bag, mostly full of underwear and Pop Tarts, and simply left. Marlene was frantic to find him. She looked everywhere but to no avail.

That was six weeks ago, and Katherine couldn't remember the last time she'd asked about him. She felt terrible.

"I'm so sorry I haven't asked, Marlene. What do you need me to pray about?" Katherine asked guiltily.

"Oh, no, that's okay, Kate. You've had a lot on your plate. I totally understand."

Marlene's gentle answer did nothing to alleviate Katherine's guilt. As a matter of fact, she felt her chest tighten with Marlene's soft words.

"We still haven't heard from him," Marlene continued, "but he's heavy on my heart today. I'm still struggling with allowing him to go without my interference, but I also know the power of prayer. I just feel like he needs it today, wherever he is, so I thought I'd call you ladies from small group.

"I finished the book last night," she went on, "and it confirmed so much for me in terms of the hard, but necessary, role we have as mothers. Because of that, I want to remain true to what God asks of me, no matter how hard it is. In the middle of that, though, my 'mommy brain' hasn't turned off, and today I felt the need to pray especially hard."

Something Marlene said caught Katherine's attention.

"What 'necessary role'?" she asked.

Marlene hesitated a beat before answering. "You know, letting them go and all that." She hesitated again for a half a second and continued. "Anyway, can you just pray that he is safe and protected?"

"Of course," Katherine said quickly, but her mind was already on what Marlene said about letting go of her child and finishing the book. "But Marlene, what did you mean by saying that the book helped you understand how we have to let go of our children? I mean, every mother knows that, right? At some point, we have to let go of them, but that doesn't make it any easier." She was getting angry again, and she had no idea why.

"That's not what I said, Kate. I said the book confirmed the role, not told me about it. It also confirmed the pain I feel in fulfilling it. That was something I needed to understand; it's something we all need to understand. All of us are having to let go of our children right now, in one season or another. And all of us are in pain because of it. Alison is dealing with Trevor and his going away to school, Marianne with her twins and their need to be independent of her and each other, and Beth still can't quite let her little one tie his own shoe. I'm sure our new friend, Cristy, is dealing with something similar, and I think that this story of Sarah will help. At least it helped me."

Katherine listened intently at Marlene's explanation, but something told her that her friend was holding back. Marlene knew something more but was unable or unwilling to tell her about it. Knowing Marlene, she wanted Katherine to figure it out on her own. Katherine decided she wasn't even going to go there with Marlene. She was too tired.

"I'm sorry about Darren, Mar. I promise to pray for him tonight," Katherine said, quickly dropping the subject of the book and everything else Marlene had been hinting at.

"Thanks. See you at our next Bible study?"

"Yeah, I'll be there."

"Okay. Good night then."

"Good night," Katherine said into the phone, even as she still felt slightly guilty at how little she had been supporting Marlene, or anyone else for that matter. She'd been so lost in her own sorrow over Nicole that she lost sight of the fact that others around her were suffering through the same sorts of struggles as mothers.

Still, that feeling quickly made its way into one of anger at her own situation. She looked up at the ceiling, often feeling that was as far as her prayers ever went, especially as they pertained to Nicole. She wanted to scream at that same ceiling, which, in her growing anger, represented where God was hiding. None of it was fair! Her heart was all about her children; it always had been. How could a loving God take one of her children out of her loving hands and put her in a place where she would get hurt? Why did none of her words help; why did none of her efforts fix the problem? Why wouldn't God show her what to do?

Sometime in the next few moments, Ken came in the room. "Who was on the phone?" he asked.

"It was just Marlene." He raised his eyebrows at her questioningly. "She wants us to pray for Darren."

"Is he still gone?"

"Yes, but she just felt today like he needed an extra dose of prayer, so she's calling those of us in our small group to pray with her." She got up as she was answering him, making her way to the bathroom to take off her makeup and put on her pajamas for bed. Ken was undressing on the other side of the bedroom.

"What's going on with everyone's kids?" he mumbled to no one in particular.

Katherine didn't acknowledge that she'd heard him. Yeah, what is going on? she thought as she shut the bathroom door.

***

"Mommy? Mom? Where are you, Mamma?"

Nicole's voice was weak and frail. Even she could hear that in her drug induced state. She was only half conscious, but she knew she was in trouble. She was cold, and she could feel hard stone beneath her half-naked body.

Why wasn't her mother here? Why hadn't she come for her? Her mom always found her, always came and took her home, but not this time. Where was she?

"Mommy?" she called again, to no one really, for no one was there with her. She was alone, left some time ago by the boy she had been so sure loved her. Turns out he hadn't cared about her at all. He'd run off at the first sign of trouble, leaving her there, too drugged to even stand, much less run out with him. She'd thought for the first couple of days that he would come back for her, but so far the only company she'd had were the rats and the drugs Adrian had left behind in his hurry to get out. But the drugs were all gone now, and the only thing Nicole had was the damp cold and the rats.

"Mamma?" she whimpered. "Where are you, Mamma?" She curled up even tighter in a ball on the floor. She absentmindedly brushed at one of the rodents making another attempt at her head. Was this where she was going to die? Had she finally gone too far?

Nicole began to weep into her arm, waiting for the inevitable pain to come. As she did so, she failed to see the figure in the corner, tears streaming down his own strong face.

He looked on with pain and love all at the same time. He had been with her from the beginning, and he would be with her to the end. He knew that there was purpose in her inner torment. It hurt him to see this beautiful one suffer, but he also knew that pain would eventually bring triumph.

"Sleep, little one," he whispered. "Sleep and know that I will never leave you."

Nicole murmured again, and he smiled with compassion at her childlike face. "There is healing ahead," he whispered again. "But for now, just sleep."

14

CHAPTER FOURTEEN

$\mathscr{B}$y the time the next Tuesday rolled around, which invariably brought with it the next ladies' Bible study meeting, Katherine had made no more headway in the book. She certainly intended to read more of it, but she was finding of late that the only thing she really wanted to do was sleep. She knew enough of depression to know that wanting to sleep a lot was one of the sure signs that one was either in a state of depression or heading straight down that road. But Katherine also found that she didn't care. She was tired. She was tired of being in pain, worrying to no avail, and seeing no end in sight to either. The clanging of the phone interrupted her thoughts.

Marlene seemed to know that Katherine might try to cancel out on going that morning. Katherine wasn't sure how Marlene always knew when she was "ghosting out on them," as Marlene liked to phrase it, and this time was no different. Katherine considered ignoring the phone, knowing it was most assuredly her friend reaffirming that she was going.

"Hey, Kate." It was the expected voice of Marlene. "I'll be there in fifteen." Then a dial tone. The woman didn't even give Katherine the opportunity to "ghost out." Marlene to a tee.

Indeed, fifteen minutes later, Marlene was at the door, that expectant look on her face, like she once again knew what Katherine might say before she said it. Katherine decided that any objections were going to be fruitless at this point. Consequently, she silently grabbed her sweater, Bible, and the book and followed Marlene out to her car.

Large group time was pretty much as expected. Susan gave her obligatory encouragements, followed up by announcements, after which they all headed to their small groups. Katherine noticed immediately that the newcomer, Bridget, had returned, but she still seemed unwilling to talk at all. It wasn't until they were well into the second question for the day that Bridget spoke up. The question they were talking about was one that had piqued Katherine's interest, too. It was at the end of the last chapter she had read in Mother Abraham after Isaac had left and Sarah was trying to figure out how to deal with what she called a "sentence of nothingness." The question read:

How would you define what Sarah referred to as her "sentence of nothingness"? Why do you think every mother comes to that at least once in the life of her child?

"I think that sometimes God asks too much of us," Bridget said, and everyone in the group looked up in surprise. "I mean, He's the one who created us to take care of our children's every need, and then He makes us ignore the very things we were created to do." She looked down at her fidgeting hands. "I think it's too much sometimes."

The only thing Katherine could think was, Thank God someone finally said it! She'd been thinking those very thoughts ever since she started reading that blasted book, but she was afraid the others would think she was being blasphemous if she dared utter them.

"I feel that sometimes, too." This time it was Marianne. "I don't know what to do about Steven and Amy. They want to be independent so badly, and I know it's got to be hard to be thirteen and twins. But it feels like I can't keep up with protecting both of them at the same time, and all the while I'm trying to protect them, they're fighting against me, each other, and every other person in their lives. How am I supposed to let go, and what does that even look like?"

That did it. The floodgates were opened, and very soon they were all talking over each other, expressing their frustrations with their children, their husbands, their families, but mostly with God. Everyone except Katherine, that is. Katherine had stopped talking, and she noticed that Bridget stopped, too.

Kelly had joined and said, "I guess I thought that since I adopted my three that it might not be so bad, but I was so wrong. I'm still their mother, and I guess that the need to protect them is in me as a woman. It isn't triggered by giving birth. It's triggered by being female."

More discussion and agreements all around. Katherine was listening, trying to take in as much as she could from these women. She was oddly encouraged that they were all feeling the same sorts of things that she had been feeling with Nicole. She was also encouraged to hear that they, too, had frustrations with God over the seemingly unfair expectations placed on them. However, even though the discussion was helping her, Katherine was still fascinated by this new woman, the one who started this present tirade but who now remained strangely silent.

Finally, Marlene noticed Bridget's silence, too, and said, "Bridget, can you tell us more about what you are feeling? What does your 'sentence of nothingness' look like?"

Bridget looked at the floor for what seemed like forever. When she looked up, they could all see the tears streaming down her face. "My son came back from the war different. He's been saved since he was ten, and he's always been in love with God and his walk with Jesus. But ever since he returned from Afghanistan, he's been different." She paused to take the Kleenex offered to her by Marianne and then continued.

"Of course, he's an adult. He doesn't even live with us anymore. He lives in Montana. But he's in pain, you know, in here," she said as she pointed to her chest. "And I can't do anything. I'm his mom, and I can't do anything!" She began to weep openly then, and Kelly and Marianne moved to her to comfort her.

"I've tried to keep the pain in my own heart at a distance," Bridget continued. "I figured that if I looked at it, then it was real. If I knew it was real, I also knew it might kill me. I joined this Bible study because I thought that maybe I'd find some peace here.

Then I started reading this book. Now it's real alright. In every word I read about Sarah, I know what I feel is real, and I can't help it! I'm really mad at God for making me go through this!"

Wow. She said that, too, Katherine thought. This woman's got some serious nerve!

"I think we all feel some semblance of that, Bridget." It was Marlene this time. Katherine knew her friend probably better than anyone in that group. Marlene would bring them to discussion instead of outbreak. She was gifted at facilitating these groups, which wasn't easy when you were dealing with women and their emotions. "So, what I think I hear you all saying, and I agree with, is that this 'sentence of nothingness' that Sarah talks about is that time when we have to deny what we feel we should be doing for our children—protect them—and instead let them go. It feels like we have been sentenced to do nothing. It literally feels like a sentence." She looked around at the group of women. "Does that about cover it?"

Nods all around. Katherine was noncommittal, but she was watching and listening intently.

"And that feels unfair," Marlene continued. "After all, God created us to take care of them. Did you know that the human infant is the most helpless of all creatures in the animal kingdom? They literally depend on their mothers for everything when they are born. No other animal in God's creation depends on its mother like humans do. Consequently, God created human mothers to be everything for their babies. He gave us that instinct, that drive to protect, nurture, care for, and love them. It's quite literally in our DNA." She paused a moment for any comment, and when there wasn't any, she went on.

"I think that's why we get so angry and frustrated when God then calls us to actually deny that which He created us to do."

"That's my point," Bridget said. "Why would He do that?"

Marlene smiled as she began gathering her books together. "Well, that is the question, isn't it?"

She stood, signaling that their time was up for the day. "Finish the book, ladies. Just like you've taken comfort from each other in that we've all shared these feelings, take comfort in the fact that Sarah, the Sarah in the Bible, most likely felt the exact same things. I promise you that there's healing in this wonderful part of her story that most never consider. We usually think of Abraham being called to sacrifice Isaac, but what of Sarah's struggle? Was she called to sacrifice him in an even higher way? How could she do that and go on?"

Marlene started heading toward the door, motioning for Katherine to follow. "Just read it. There are answers there for all of us."

Katherine quickly got up and followed Marlene out to the car. They rode back to Katherine's house in silence. Katherine knew better than to probe Marlene for answers right then. Marlene would only answer her in vague notions. She would want Katherine to find her own answers, so Katherine didn't even attempt the shortcut.

Once they got to her house, Katherine did look at Marlene and say, "I appreciate you, Mar."

She didn't wait for her friend to answer. She simply opened the door and went into the house. Suddenly, the only thing she wanted to do was read. She needed to know what Sarah found out. Unfortunately once she got in the house, she remembered that there were a few things she needed at the grocery store. She'd have to go there first. Then she could come home and read another chapter or two of her book. She made a quick list and headed out the door. She hated to admit it, but maybe there was a light at the end of this tunnel called despair. Dare she hope for it? It was with those thoughts in her head that she made her way to the store.

***

As Katherine walked down aisle after aisle at the store, she couldn't get her mind off of the discussion at Bible study that morning. Did God really intend that every mother go through this kind of pain with her children? If so, why would He do that?

She remembered dozens of lessons she'd heard from the pulpit about God's purposes in all things, how He made beauty from ashes and restored all that the locusts had eaten, but those had all just been handy dandy phrases, hadn't they? Weren't they just those convenient tools that every good preacher could pull out of his proverbial hat when he needed to justify bad things happening to good people?

That had always been Katherine's opinion. After all, she'd never really considered nor seen, if truth be told, a time when anything beautiful came of the charred ruins of someone's life. She'd read stories, but she'd never seen it.

She was so deep in thought, now walking aimlessly down the cereal aisle, that she ran headlong into someone. "Oh," she exclaimed and found herself looking into the bluest eyes she'd ever seen. "I'm so sorry," she muttered, backing away quickly and looking down at her feet, filled with embarrassment.

"Oh, no worries," he said as he smiled.

He was handsome, but not overtly so. He was about her age, she guessed, and there were thin smile lines around the corners of those amazing eyes. She couldn't help herself; she was staring.

"Do I know you?" she finally asked, after what she knew was a weird amount of time. She was lost in those eyes.

"You may," he answered with a smile. "I know a lot of people."

She looked down at the ground for a second but then quickly looked back at him. She found herself somewhat mesmerized by this man. It's not that she was physically attracted to him or anything. There was just something about him that captivated her.

"I feel like I've seen you somewhere before," she said again, still trying to figure out why she couldn't look away from those eyes. "Do you work at the church?"

Suddenly, he was laughing. She smiled, despite herself, since she didn't know what she had said that could possibly have been that funny.

"I've done some work there," he finally answered, "but I wouldn't say I work there." He giggled again and went on, "I work at a lot of places, I guess you could say."

"Oh," she stammered, finally pulling her gaze away from his face. "I guess I've probably just seen you around."

"Yes, I believe you have," he said.

"Well," she giggled, in spite of herself again, "maybe I'll see you around then."

He smiled as she turned to leave, but she stopped short when she heard his next words.

"There's purpose in the nothingness."

She whipped around, speaking before she even got all the way. "What did you say?" But he wasn't there. They had been talking halfway down the cereal aisle, so she didn't understand for the life of her how he could have disappeared so quickly, but he was gone.

She walked quickly to the end of the aisle, making her way to the right and to the left, sure she would see him looking at a box of rice or even making his way to the checkout counter. But he was gone. It was like he had simply vanished. Had she just imagined what she thought she heard him say?

There's purpose in the nothingness.

It seemed like such an odd thing to say, given the circumstances, but Katherine couldn't deny the poignant timing of hearing a sentence like that. Undeterred, she walked up and down every aisle in the store, absolutely positive she would find him, but he wasn't anywhere. He was just gone.

Katherine absentmindedly went to the checkout counter herself. She paid for the few groceries she had in her cart and walked out to her SUV. Still trying to make sense of what just happened, she unloaded the bags and got behind the wheel. She thought briefly of calling Marlene and telling her what had happened, but she figured she would just sound silly.

But it wasn't silly. Deep inside, Katherine knew that running into this stranger with the mesmerizing blue eyes was anything but silly. Something profound had just happened, and though she couldn't quite put her finger on the significance of it, she wasn't about to let the memory of it escape her further attention.

There's purpose in the nothingness.

She thought about this as she drove home, now even more intent than ever to read the rest of Sarah's journey in Mother Abraham. Somehow she knew that all of it was tied together somehow.

He watched her pull out of the grocery store parking lot from across the street. He was still smiling at her question. "Do I work at the church?" he laughed to himself. He was still giggling as he walked away, headed to the worst part of town to watch over his beautiful one. It was almost time.

15

MOTHER ABRAHAM

CHAPTER FIFTEEN

- CHAPTER 4 -

Let your steadfast love comfort me according to your promise to your servant.

Psalms 119:76 (ESV)

As Sarah was making her way back from the traders, her mind was still ill at ease. Certainly there were many things within the running of their people that should take up space in her head, but she felt sick at the center of her being over what was being required of her son, of her husband, and of her.

The God of her husband had been faithful to them, in all of their trials and struggles, even granting to them a treasured son in their old age. This God had begun as the One her husband pledged himself to, but she, too, had developed her own faith in Him as their Provider. Their God had demanded much of them in the past in the way of believing in His promises to them, even when those very promises seemed quite impossible to reach. Yet, reach them they had, every last one of them, so that even now they led a mighty legion of people in their camp. No, Sarah knew she could not, should not, deny the sovereign love and protection of YHWH, but here she was, doing so anyway.

She wrestled with these feelings of resentment, confusion, even hostility toward their Father. Why was He taking away the very gift He had promised would make her husband's heirs as vast as the sands of the seashore? Abraham had recounted to her the promises of YHWH. Her husband recounted to her how the Father told him to look toward the heavens and number the stars. In their number, God told her husband that he would find the number of his offspring. This, He promised, would come through Isaac, not Ishmael, the son of Hagar. No, God promised that these heirs would come through her and Abraham. How would this happen if Isaac was taken from them?

And what of her husband? Was his faith in his God so blind that he would willingly and without question offer up their precious son as a sacrifice? How could he do such a thing? Why did he seem not to suffer this pain as she presently did? Was her love for their son greater than her husband's?

Even as Sarah walked and pondered these things, she knew that she was behaving as the foolish girls did among them. She, the wife of the great Abraham, knew better. She knew the love of God and the provision from Him. Even as she questioned her Father, she repented of this foolishness. She begged His forgiveness for questioning both Him and His motives in anything He chose to do.

And yet, the battle in her mind raged on. She teetered back and forth between loyalty to the God of her husband and confusion over what this same God was asking of her. So great was the torment within her that she feared she might be physically ill before reaching the seclusion of her tent. She began to quicken her step, knowing that with every footfall she may not make it back before the entire camp saw the state of her.

As she rounded the last of the tents of her maid servants, she saw something very unexpected. Sitting just outside of her tent, stoking a small fire with a long-necked brass pot perched above it, was a man. Sarah immediately recognized the pot as the one she personally used to brew her favorite tea.

"Hello, stranger," she began, trying to sound cordial but quite incensed at his supposition that he could go through her things. "May I help you with something?" She was finding it difficult to keep her tone civil. Who was this stranger that he would behave so brazenly?

But then he turned to face her, and all her negative feelings flew away in an instant. The only thing she felt was wonder and intrigue. His eyes, she thought. They are as blue as the Great Sea!

"Hello, Sarah," he said in a voice so melodious that Sarah's breath caught in her chest. "I hope you don't mind that I helped myself to your pot." He smiled again, that very disarming smile. "Would you like some? Please pardon me, but you look as though a cup of tea might help calm you."

Sarah looked down, trying rather unsuccessfully to gather her composure. "No, thank you, sir," she finally stammered out. Before she could think, however, she was staring into his eyes again, lost in their color and beauty. She sat on a rug opposite him and the fire, never allowing her gaze to break his. Who is this man? she thought, but she couldn't manage to say anything audibly.

"I'm sure you are wondering who I am, sister," he said as he sat opposite her. "You may call me Arella, though I go by many names." He smiled again and continued. "I have come to bring you a message, dear one, a message that I pray will satiate your troubled heart."

Still mesmerized by his gaze, Sarah managed to ask, "My troubled heart, sir? How might you know of any troubles within my heart?"

He laughed and said, "I know only what is revealed to me, and your heart has been so revealed." He stoked the fire under the pot, lifted it off of the coals on which it sat, and poured two cups of the steaming liquid into the cups he had set before him. He placed one in front of Sarah and the other in front of himself. However, he made no move to drink his. Instead, he motioned for her to take hers, and she complied easily.

Sarah took a sip, and never had any liquid soothed her as this did. It was unlike any tea she had ever drank, and though she wanted to ask him about it, she was loath to interrupt him as he began to speak again.

"Sister, I cannot explain to you the ways of YHWH, nor can I give you assurance about what you will see and hear. I come only to give you foreknowledge that you are favored among God's creation. He loves you, as He loves your husband. Indeed, He chose you just as He chose Abraham."

"How is it, sir, that you know so much about my husband and myself?" Sarah asked.

"As I said, I know only that which has been revealed," the stranger answered. "Today I come to you simply to encourage your troubled heart and to tell you that YHWH favors you. Indeed, you will soon know the depth of His love for you."

Sarah looked down then. She truly did not feel loved at that moment. She had so many questions for this stranger who seemed to know the Father's heart better than she did. She wanted answers, but she was afraid to ask the truest questions in her mind. Without consciously coming to any conclusions, Sarah knew this was no ordinary encounter.

Arella smiled. "His love looks differently than humans surmise. You have questions about your son and about how YHWH loves. Be encouraged, favored one. He will come to you."

When he said this, he stood and moved to leave.

"Wait!" Sarah screamed and then looked around to be sure no one else heard her outburst. As she scanned the others near her tent, she was surprised to see that none of them seemed at all concerned about this strange man making tea outside of their mistress's tent. As a matter of fact, none of them even looked her way.

Arella paused without turning and spoke one last thing before leaving. "There is purpose in the nothingness, favored one."

***

Katherine dropped the book onto her lap as her mouth dropped open. What had she just read? What was going on here?

She looked at the cover of the book again, with that benign stock image of a Middle Eastern woman in supposed distress. They really should come up with a different cover. She tossed the book to the side, still staring at it as if it would suddenly sprout arms and legs and a mouth and start talking to her.

She nudged herself off of the bed, never taking her eyes off of the book, and went into the bathroom, splashing cold water onto her face. Looking at herself in the mirror, she said aloud, "Pull it together, girl. Pull...it... together."

She towel dried her face and went back into her bedroom, locking her eyes on the book as soon as she could. She didn't go back to her bed right away. She stopped about three feet away and kept looking at the face of the woman on the cover.

Did she and Sarah see the same man? No way! That's impossible! For a second she thought about giving the book back to Marlene, but then her curiosity got the best of her. She had to keep reading. But still, how had the man in the book said the same words Katherine could have sworn she heard the man in the grocery store say to her just a few hours before?

"There's purpose in the nothingness."

Maybe she had already read that part and simply forgot. Then it was possible that she had imagined hearing those words since she'd already read them. She was feeling a strange kinship with Sarah, so it wasn't out of the question that she might be filling in the blanks in her reality with things she was reading in the book. She might even have imagined that the man in the store had crazy blue eyes that she couldn't look away from. Maybe that image was in her brain from reading about him in the book. Yeah, maybe there was an explanation for what she knew was simply unexplainable.

But she hadn't read that chapter yet. She was sure of it. She would have remembered the details, the scenes, the people. Katherine hated reading books more than once. She never understood how people could ever enjoy that. If she had read something, she remembered it and would skip either the whole book or the parts she had already read. She considered rereading something she had already read a waste of time, and besides, it bored her. She was even like that with television shows and movies. She absolutely couldn't stand seeing something more than once. She'd always rather skip it and move onto something new.

No, Katherine hadn't already read that chapter. Otherwise, she would have remembered while reading it and skipped on to the next chapter.

So what was the explanation? How had she met someone so eerily similar to the man Sarah encountered, and how had he said the very same words to her as the man in the book had said to Sarah?

Very slowly, Katherine crossed the couple of feet that lay between her and the bed. Never taking her eyes off of the book, she laid back down, pulled the covers up around her waist, and reached over to pick it up. It felt heavier than before, though she knew that had to be her imagination. It was the same book, but maybe it was the weight of what was happening to her that made it feel heavier.

With more than a little trepidation, she thumbed through the last pages she had been reading, finding the spot where she'd stopped. She couldn't deny that she was feeling weirdly drawn to keep reading. She had a feeling that whatever was about to happen to Sarah was going to have great significance for her, too.

Katherine took a deep breath, closed her eyes for a second or two, and started to read.

***

Arella paused without turning and spoke one last thing before leaving. "There is purpose in the nothingness, favored one." Then with two strides, he disappeared behind the side of her tent. Sarah got up as quickly as her legs would allow to go after him, but as she rounded the tent, she saw that he was gone. She looked around every side and still found nothing. He had simply vanished.

She and Abraham had been visited by angels before, but never had she been visited alone. The time she remembered vividly was outside of the Oaks of Mamre when the three holy men of heaven had first appeared to her husband, one of whom Abraham later told her was the Lord Himself!

Abraham had run to her immediately, telling her to prepare bread and curds of milk for three strangers who had come to him. She had listened to their conversation inside the door of her tent and heard them promise a child to be born of her and Abraham a year later. Sarah knew that was impossible, even laughable, and she had indeed laughed. She was horrified when the men heard her, even asking why she was laughing. She denied it out of sheer embarrassment, but they had known of her unbelief. And yet a year later, she bore Isaac, the promised heir.

Of course, Sarah couldn't be sure that Arella was an angel, but she did know that this meeting had been extraordinary. He had behaved as these three men had behaved all those years ago, and she couldn't deny the feeling he invoked in her. She had felt a modicum of fear, but mostly she felt at ease in his presence. Yes, this had been a holy meeting, but had he been a holy man of heaven?

As she was taking a third trek around her tent, making sure she hadn't missed him somehow, Talitha came walking up to Sarah. "Mistress Sarah, may I help you find something?" she asked, looking in the direction Sarah had been looking.

"I'm looking for the man who was just here. Did you see him leave?"

"Man?" Talitha asked incredulously. "I saw no man, mistress."

"Of course you did," Sarah scolded. "You were standing only a few steps from my tent. He was here." Sarah pointed to the spot where the fire still smoldered. "He built this fire and made a pot of tea."

Talitha looked obediently in all directions, though her look was one of pity when she finally made eye contact once again with Sarah. "I saw no man, Mistress," she said softly again. "Perhaps you would like to lie down for a bit." She tried to steer Sarah toward the tent opening. "It's getting late, and you have been under a lot of stress."

Sarah resisted the gentle nudge and looked at Talitha with new understanding. "You didn't see him, did you?"

Talitha shook her head slowly.

Sarah stood up completely and straightened her skirt. "I'll be in my tent," she said as she walked purposefully toward the open flap. She could feel her maid servant staring after her, probably still wearing that look of sadness for her mistress. Sarah, on the other hand, had at least part of her answer. If Talitha hadn't seen him, then that would explain why no one else around her tent paid the least attention to his presence. None of them had seen him, only her.

Arella was a holy man of heaven. And he had paid her a visit. He also told her that YHWH was coming to her. What could that mean? Would the Creator Father come to her, a mere woman in a tent in the middle of the desert? YHWH spoke to Abraham, not her.

Sarah laid down on the palate of blankets on the floor of the tent she shared with her husband. It was late, and she was very tired. Actually, she was more tired than she remembered ever being. It came on very suddenly, and before she knew it, Sarah could hardly keep her eyes open. As her heavy lids closed, she thought of the last words Arella had spoken to her.

There is purpose in the nothingness.

Eventually, she found sleep, finding herself in a place that would change the course of her perceptions from that moment on into eternity.

16

CHAPTER SIXTEEN

For a second time, Katherine dropped the book in her lap. She had always prided herself on being a woman of reason. She wasn't given to flights of fancy or weird notions of other-worldly visitations. Katherine had heard enough of that growing up. She was determined to live her life with her feet planted squarely on terra firma.

At that same time, she simply couldn't deny what she'd just read, and she couldn't deny this strange coincidence, if, in fact, that's what it was. This blue-eyed Arella in the book said the exact same words to Sarah as the blue-eyed stranger had said to her in the store. Suddenly, Katherine's rigid world of no-nonsense reality started to rock.

Katherine's faith had never been much to write home about. She went to church and joined all the right studies. She sang in the choir and went to the socials. She believed in God and in Jesus, and she had accepted Christ as her personal Savior when she was a teenager. It's just that her faith had never really been palpable. It wasn't something that moved her or drove her. It just kind of was. Which is exactly why entertaining the notion that she was in the middle of a faith-driven encounter was a bit more than she could digest. Only good people had this kind of thing happen to them. You know, like missionaries and pastors and theologians. Visitations and words from God didn't come to people like her, did they? Why would God waste His time on the likes of her?

None of it made sense, and Katherine began to get a headache from simply thinking about it. She knew she had to keep reading. How in the world could she stop now?

Katherine stared at the woman on the cover again, her mind a blur at the possibilities of what might be happening. She began thumbing through the book again, this time with more urgency, trying to find the beginning of the next chapter. Part of her still wanted to give the book back to Marlene, but the louder part told her she must keep reading.

Meanwhile, on the other side of town, another battle was being waged. As Katherine sought answers to her own feelings, her daughter sought deliverance from her own pain.

***

Something pulling at her legs. Rough hands under her arms. Muffled voices and the sound of wheels rolling closer to her.

"What's happening," Nicole whimpered, only half conscious. "What's going on?"

Voices again, too low for her to understand, and then she was moving. She tried to open her eyes, but they were so heavy.

"Get an IV started and call Corner Mountain General. Inform that Narcan was administered and patient is en route."

Nicole was beginning to come to, but only in time to feel an oxygen mask placed over her mouth.

"Hang in there, honey," said a female to her right. She was moving again, and she felt suddenly like she might be sick. "Just hang in there. We're going to get you some help."

More movement, a slight jolt, and then she felt more stable, like she was on a bed or something. Then she heard sirens, though they seemed very far away. She wanted to ask where they were going, who needed the ambulance, and were her friends alright. Where was Adrian? But she couldn't make any more words come out. Instead, she was vaguely aware of the sound of her own moaning.

"Be calm, little one." This voice was directly in her ear, and it was different than the rest. She immediately felt her pulse slow and her breathing less erratic. "I am here," the voice whispered again. "I will not leave you. Be at peace." And she was at peace, if only for the moment.

"Back away, sir," said the female paramedic. "Who did you say you were?"

"I am her, um, uncle," he said. The paramedic looked at him in wonder. She looked momentarily confused, and then resignation settled on her face.

"Well, sir, please sit back so that we can do our work."

He did sit back, smiling serenely as he did. The peace he spoke over his charge now settled over the paramedics, like a soft rain settles on an entire meadow. Nicole began to breathe more regularly, and the work of the paramedics, only moments before frenzied, now became structured movements of precision and confidence.

The stranger stroked Nicole's hand as the ambulance screamed toward Copper Mountain Community Hospital. He, too, felt serene. His orders had finally come, and he had work to do.

MOTHER ABRAHAM

CHAPTER SEVENTEEN

- CHAPTER 5 -

I will bless you with a future filled with hope—a future of success, not of suffering.
You will turn back to me and ask for help, and I will answer your prayers.
Jeremiah 29:11-12 (CEV)

Though Sarah's eyelids were heavy, sleep didn't come quickly. She tossed and turned, staring blankly at the top of her tent for what seemed like an eternity. The strange man calling himself Arella would not leave the forefront of her thoughts. Who was he really? How had he come to be in front of her tent while no one else seemed to see him? What did he mean when he told her that YHWH would come to her?

There weren't answers to any of these questions, at least not answers she could find, but her mind refused to dismiss them. Arella had known of her pain and of her faltering faith. He'd known that she was battling these empty feelings of nothingness and despair over what she was sure was transpiring with her son. Then he'd said that there was meaning in her feelings, in the nothingness. How could there be meaning in nothing?

Finally, as unconsciousness overtook her exhausted mind, she drifted to sleep with Arella's face behind her eyes.

"Hello, daughter."

Her eyes snapped open as she heard this voice, a deep, melodic voice, from the darkest corner of the tent.

"Who's there? Who has come into my tent?" she asked in a hushed whisper. She could think of no servant or member of their clan who would dare venture into her tent without being invited, especially while her husband was away.

She was looking into the corner intently, desperately trying to make out the features of the figure she could see in the shadows.

"How dare you come into my tent," she exclaimed, trying very unsuccessfully to sound in control and strong. Truthfully, even the sound of this man's voice made her insides tremble. "Come into the light so that I may see who will incur the wrath of my husband!"

The figure stepped silently toward her, first revealing a weather-worn sandal and white tunic. She quickly saw that he had a brown cloth wrapped around his waist and draped over his right shoulder. He didn't rush at her, nor did he seem to be moving too slowly. He simply stepped as if he belonged there, with a familiarity that both confused and intrigued her.

In another step, she could see his head, framed by shoulder-length brown hair that fell gracefully over his shoulders. But she didn't remain fixed on those attributes for long. It was his face that caused her breath to catch in her lungs. He was beautiful, but not in a feminine way. He was simply the most beautiful human she had ever seen.

His eyes were almost translucent, and she couldn't quite make out the color. It was as if every color of the rainbow were there, each flickering in the translucence, radiating a new color that hadn't been seen before. His skin was ruddy, but flawless, and his mouth was curled upward in the most serene smile Sarah had ever seen. He stopped after he was in the light enough for her to make out his appearance, standing quietly for a few seconds so that Sarah could remember to begin breathing again.

"Hello, Sarah," he said, and his voice was like a song, Sarah thought. She knew that he wasn't actually singing, but it affected her as if he were. The sound of his voice floated on the air and landed on her like a warm blanket, falling around her, enveloping her in calm and peace. She'd never felt anything like it before, and any sense of indignant rage or fear of danger disappeared immediately. There was just this man and the melody of his voice.

"May I sit?" he asked as he motioned toward one of the larger seating pillows near the entry to the tent. She nodded in an almost imperceptive trance, never taking her eyes off of his. He smiled bigger and sat down.

With his legs crossed and his arms draped over his knees, he looked at her again, and again she forgot to breathe. Who was this man? Why was she so at ease in the presence of a stranger in her tent in the middle of the night, especially a male stranger?

"Please forgive me for coming to you this way, daughter," his melodious voice began again. "I certainly do not want to frighten you."

She shook her head as if to indicate that she wasn't frightened and that it was alright that he was there. Neither of which should be true, but they were nonetheless.

"Who are you?" Sarah was surprised at the sound of her own voice. She hadn't thought that speech was possible for her at that moment, but it was indeed her voice she heard ask this strange, beautiful man who he was.

He laughed a little, looking at his lap as he did. The sound that came from this man's mirth made Sarah's head swim, but not in confusion or pain. Her head swam in the sheer enjoyment of hearing it. The very sound of his laughter was more wonderful than even the sound of his voice. It was like the sound of a thousand ripples of water on a parched, desert afternoon. Or the melody of a hundred perfect voices, raising a song in complete harmony in worship. She would have eagerly given her very existence in that instance to only hear him laugh again.

He looked up at her, and Sarah found herself holding her breath this time. He looked into her heart with those translucent eyes, and she longed to hear him speak.

"I am the One who loves you, Sarah, and I am here so that I might give you strength that must endure for generations to come."

Answering for Sarah was now out of the question. She knew only that she wanted to hear anything and everything this stranger had to say.

"I am, dear one, and I love. It is in that love that I do all that is and all that will be. It is the width and breadth of every decision I make. My love for you and for all of my children is the driving force for all of existence. I do and am all that is necessary and needed for them." He stopped and looked down again. Suddenly, Sarah felt his pain, and her own heart threatened to break in the feeling of it.

"Please hear me when I tell you that I incur no joy when my beloved ones suffer. I feel your pain and your misery, while I desire only joy and peace for you. It is, however, this very desire for joy and peace on your behalf that also drives me to bring my plans for you to fruition." He stopped again and looked into her eyes once more. "That is true for all of you, dear one."

Suddenly Sarah knew instinctively that his next words were going to catapult her to a deeper knowledge, but this knowledge would also threaten to destroy her heart if she chose not to hear it.

"Sarah," he began, and she felt her head spin in hearing him simply say her name. "My Sarah, you are mother. You are one of my most precious creations, more intricate than the most extraordinary desert flower and more prized than all the precious jewels of this world. I gave to you the role I hold close to my heart, closer than just about any other. You nurture and hold, you protect and defend, you love and cherish in ways that most closely mirror mine. I have given you a job that is so very important as you bring forth kingdom workers and dwellers in the midst of a perverse and needy generation. I created you to bring them safely to me."

He stood and moved toward her, never losing eye contact as he did.

"I created you to bring them safely to me."

He reached out to clasp her hands in his as he repeated these last words. "Do you understand me, Sarah?" he asked gently. "Do you understand the depth of what I am telling you?"

Sarah nodded slowly. She did understand, but the tears were falling freely down her face now. With her understanding came a sadness she hadn't known possible.

He ran a soft thumb across her tear-stained cheek, cupping her face in his strong hand as he did so. His own tears ran freely, as well, matching her pain as he continued. "Yes, you comprehend, my love."

Then he lifted her face softly up so that they were staring into one another's eyes, now only inches apart. "Sarah," he began again. "Now I must say to you what I came to say, and it will require of you great strength, perhaps greater strength than is present in all of my creation. I made you with this strength. I destined you, mother, to embody all that is required for the task at hand. This is your high calling."

Sarah was completely torn in this moment. She wanted with everything in her to hear this man speak to her, but in another part of her heart, she knew that what he was about to tell her would be the most devastating thing she will have ever heard. That part of her wished him to leave and never return.

But she knew she would never send him away. This man, this perfect being, was all of her. She knew that, even as he spoke his next words, words that would begin a course for mothers for all earthly time.

"My beautiful one, if I choose Isaac's death, you must be at peace with that."

Sarah didn't respond. She was sure she must have heard this man incorrectly. He could not have said what she thought she heard him say.

He sighed and dropped his hand from her face, slowly moving away from her. "Yes, beloved, you have heard me correctly." He looked at her again, this time with supreme sadness behind his mirrored eyes. But there was also resolute strength there, a strength that comes from definitive authority. She knew he was speaking truth to her, but it hurt him to hurt her.

He stood more erectly then, and though tears were still on his high cheeks, he spoke in a deep and resonating voice. "If I choose to allow your son to die, you must be at peace with that. And you can be, daughter. You can be because I have given you the strength of a thousand lions, the steadfastness of the greatest mountain, the endurance of the strongest of all creatures. I made you, my love, and gave you the instinct to protect and guide the most helpless. But I also gave you the strength to give them back to me when it was time, no matter what that must look like.

"I have called you to something higher and more profound than almost anything else I have created. I have called you to honor your creation, even as you more highly honor your Creator. This is truly a high calling, which is why I created you as mother."

Sarah finally found her voice. "I don't understand."

"Oh, but I think you do, beloved," he said, looking intently into her eyes again. "You know what I have asked of you, even as you mourn Isaac's departure now."

Sarah began to weep, unable and unwilling to hold back the tears now. "So my Isaac is to be sacrificed then? You will take him from me?"

"You make many assumptions, dear one. The issue at hand here is your heart as it is knit to mine. I do not address my intentions with Isaac, only your heart and your will to be relinquished to mine.

"Let me ask you, from where did Isaac come, truly?"

Sarah looked down. "From YHWH," she answered begrudgingly.

"Yes, that he did," he said. "To whom shall he go when he leaves this world?"

"To YHWH," she answered again.

"Indeed, it is so. He will return to the place from which he came, to the arms from whom he was born. Now, beloved, I ask you to consider that the time in between is also for YHWH, even as it is for all that He has created, yes?"

"It is so," Sarah whispered again.

"If this is so, then this time on earth is a time that is entrusted to others to keep YHWH's children safe, to protect them and care for them with almost complete disregard for anything other than this charge. This task can only be given to those highly trusted, to those highly called.

"It is to this that I have called mothers, and this is no average calling. No, this call can only be answered by the strongest of my created, those beloved who will do what they are made to do and then trust me enough to do the unthinkable—to let go. I call them to trust that I am love, and I am trustworthy. Therefore, they are the only ones who have the ability to deny that which they were created to do, and so relinquish to me the providence over that which is mine."

Sarah began to sob in earnest now. With all of the love and devotion she felt for this man before her, she couldn't keep the pain at losing Isaac at bay in the face of what was being asked of her. "But he's my son, my only miracle-boy," she cried. "How can I do such a thing?"

Once again, the man was in front of her, though she never saw him move. He just simply was there, holding her hands in his, his gentle face again only inches from hers. "Ah, my love, but the truth is that he is my son whom I shared with you for a time. I shared him with you because my trust in you is exceptional. I shared my son with you because I trust you, mother. I trust you.

"I ask in return that you trust me. Trust that I will not leave him nor will I forsake him. Trust that I have a plan, and that plan will always be for Isaac's good, just as it is for you and all of my children. Trust that even though you may not understand my ways, that they are exponentially higher than you can ever imagine. I'll finish what I started, and I will bring his joy to completion."

He lifted her chin to meet his once again and softly said, "You see, beloved, this high call is about your heart knit to my heart which is bound to Isaac's heart. Can you trust in that, no matter what it may look like now?"

Sarah met his gaze and stared deep into the translucence of what she saw there. It was overwhelming. She was met with a sea of peace and love that she could never have imagined possible. She saw in this man's eyes her very own soul, and in that place she also saw rest. Sarah finally realized that she was in the presence of YHWH, though in some part of her mind she knew this was a vision, and he certainly must not look as this man did. Still, YHWH was speaking to her, giving her direction so that she could pave the way for mothers to come, mothers everywhere who were going to be called to the same impossible call now in front of her. YHWH not only trusted her with Isaac, but he also trusted her with the first acceptance of this divine call. In that instance, Sarah knew what was expected of her, and she knew that just as she was truly loved, so was Isaac.

"Yes, Divine One, I understand, and I will do it." She bowed her head and rested them on the tops of his hands as they grasped hers. He kissed the top of her head and sighed again.

"Sarah, mother, honored one, strength and dignity shall be your clothing. Wisdom and the teaching of kindness shall be on your tongue, and your child will rise and call you blessed. Now, mother, arise, and walk in the high calling in which only you can walk. Now, from this day forward, your husband will be known as Father Abraham, the father of a vast and great nation, the father of my people. But you, beloved, are mother. Your sacrifice will be no less difficult than Abraham's, but it will be less understood. He is Father Abraham, and you are Mother."

Sarah felt a rush of wind whirl in the tent, and she briefly wondered who had opened the flap. She looked up sharply, intending to shoo away the intruder, but when she did, her surroundings had changed. No longer was she standing in the middle of her tent, head bowed onto the hands of her very Creator. Instead, her eyes opened with a start, and she was once more lying on the pallet she and Abraham had shared for many years. The sun was only just then shining through the slit in the opening to her tent.

Sarah sat up with a start, instinctively wiping her eyes and opening them again to be sure she was awake. She looked intently around the tent, searching for some sign that the man was still there, had actually been there. But he wasn't; she was completely alone with only the sounds of a waking clan beginning outside of her tent.

She, however, was waking in a much different way. She had awakened with the understanding that she was mother, and in that, she was highly favored.

MOTHER ABRAHAM

18

CHAPTER EIGHTEEN

*N*icole was floating somewhere between consciousness and a dream. She was vaguely aware of voices around her, but they seemed so very far away. Even the pain she had been feeling only a short time before seemed very distant. The only thing that mattered was this ambiguous dream state she was in.

She was also aware of the fact that she wasn't alone. Though she couldn't see anyone else, she knew he was there, the man who had whispered into her ear before. She didn't know exactly who he was, but at the same time, he seemed very familiar to her.

"I'm here, dear one." It was him, but he wasn't actually in the room with her, at least not where anyone else might see him. Nicole knew on some subconscious level that he was talking to her in her mind.

"Who are you?" she asked, but again, her lips weren't moving. This felt like a strange dream, one from which she truly didn't want to wake.

"I am sent," he answered.

"Sent for what?" she continued.

"Why, for you, of course," he said with what sounded like a chuckle.

"Why?"

"Because you are loved."

Tears stung Nicole's eyes, and someone in the distance wiped them away with a piece of gauze. "No, I'm not," she countered, and even in this dream state, Nicole could feel herself crying. "I've done too much. I've hurt too many people. It's too late for me to be loved," she continued. "I'm broken, worthless, just too used up."

"Oh, my dear one," he said soothingly, "there is no such thing as what you speak of. Love is more than payment for good deeds. Indeed, it is beyond what you do. You are loved, Nicole, because the Source of all things chose to love you. He loves you, and therefore, your worth has been bought with that love, not by the things you may have done or not done in your past."

She was trying hard to see him in her head, but the only thing she could actually do in this state was hear and feel. Her sight did not play a part in whatever was going on in her mind right then.

"I don't understand," she finally said. "How can someone love me when they don't know me?"

"Oh, but you are known, dear one. Indeed, you were known before time itself. You were known and loved even before you were. And this, my beloved, is why I was sent. I am here to bring you to your journey."

"My journey?"

"Yessssss, your journeeeeey." His voice began to trail away, as if he were moving to a distance. "You will see soon." He was only a whisper now. "I will be there to show you, but you will see beyond me." Nicole could barely hear him at that point. He was almost gone.

"Wait!" she screamed in her head, but it was too late. He was gone again. She could feel the vacancy left where his presence had once been.

"She's waking up. Someone get the doctor!"

Nicole began to make out new voices, along with the clanging of metal against metal and the sound of many footfalls around her. Faintly in the background, she could hear the steady beeping of the heart monitor machine and the hum of the oxygen now blowing gently into her mouth through the mask on her face.

"Wait." Her voice sounded weak, even to herself. "Don't leave me yet."

"We're not going anywhere, sweetheart," said the nurse by the side of her bed. "We are here. No one is leaving you."

Nicole started shaking her head weakly from side to side, trying to tell them that they were misunderstanding her. However, the nurse simply spoke more soothingly to her, trying to calm her down.

Nicole knew then that she was fully awake and in some sort of hospital. The dream man was gone, but the pain was back. Her insides felt like someone had taken them all out and then hurriedly put them back in whatever fashion suited them. Her head felt like it might explode, and she was actively trying not to vomit with every passing second.

"Shhhh, there, there, sweetheart," the nurse said again as she continued to wipe Nicole's forehead with a damp cloth. "It's okay. You're going to be okay. You gave us quite a scare, but you're okay now."

Nicole began to settle, breathing more deeply through the oxygen mask. She was slipping back into unconsciousness again, but this time from sheer exhaustion. She just wanted to sleep, to sleep and then wake up in her own room where none of what had happened over the last few weeks was real. Instead, she wanted to wake up and realize it had all been a terrible dream.

Except for the part with the dream man and what he had said to her. He called her "dear one" and told her that she was loved. He also told her that she was going on a journey. She didn't feel like going on a journey just then, but somehow she also knew the dream man wasn't talking about any ordinary journey. This journey would be different—different and wonderful.

As she drifted into sleep, she murmured out loud, "I'm going on a journey, and I am loved." And then she was out.

The nurse was still wiping her brow, but she smiled at these last words. She had no idea what the girl was talking about. It was most likely just remnants of a bad trip on whatever drugs she'd been immersing herself in over the last few weeks, but the words made the nurse smile nonetheless.

"Sleep now, little girl. I don't know about any journey, but I bet you are loved."

The nurse didn't see the blue-eyed stranger enter the room. No one else did either, but he was there, standing only a few feet away from his charge.

He smiled again. It felt good to do so after so much heartache in the years preceding. It wasn't that his faith had left him as he waited. He knew that all would work out for her good, as had been promised. They always did for those who had received His love. The path, however, was often hard, and it was painful to watch.

"It won't be long, dear one," Arella said softly. "It won't be long now."

19

CHAPTER NINETEEN

On the other side of town, Katherine was staring incredulously at the now closed book lying on her lap. What had she just read? In all her years, Katherine had never felt so, for lack of a better phrase, out of control. She simply couldn't believe all that had happened, and she certainly couldn't believe what was right before her eyes.

She and this character had shared an encounter with, what? An angel? Had it been this same blue-eyed man in the supermarket that she read about just now in this fictional account of Sarah, the wife of Abraham…from the Bible?!

Katherine's logical brain told her that these were all just a series of amazing coincidences and nothing more. Her logic told her that she was tired and worn out from all the stress of Nicole and her marriage and her crumbling fortress of a home she'd hidden behind for so long. Her need for order and predictableness screamed for her to stop this train of thought, because if she continued going down this road, she was going to have to accept all kinds of things as reality that she quite frankly had avoided for a lot of years.

She made herself breathe more slowly, more deliberately, gaining more and more control of her emotions as she did so. Her heart began to slow down, and she eventually looked down at the book again, trying to see her situation from fresh eyes.

But even as she did so, she knew she had entered a brand new place in her spirituality. This brand new place was certainly going to redefine her role as mother, as wife, as friend, and most importantly, as a believer. What had never been necessarily real to her was now glaringly real. Try as she might, Katherine simply could not deny that she had experienced something profound in the reading of Mother Abraham. Her eyes had been opened, but so had her heart.

Truth be told, Katherine was tired of fighting against what was obviously truth. She had been fighting against it for a long time in favor of "logic" and "clear thinking." Look where that had gotten her. She was miserable, her husband was miserable, her daughter was lost, and her poor boy was neglected.

She'd fought against these truths because they didn't fit into her ordered world. Sure, she had always attended church, sang in the choir, and gone to Bible study. She'd even done her due diligence in serving at vacation Bible school a time or two. But those were things she had done. They weren't things she believed, at least not down deep. The problem was that all that doing hadn't helped her one bit when life turned upside down. There were no answers in doing things, so she had simply lost herself entirely in the losing of her daughter, so much so that she had almost lost her husband and her sweet boy, too.

Motherhood was just another riddle that eventually she couldn't solve, another task that left her alone and angry when nothing turned out the way she thought it should.

But now, now she had answers to this riddle, though the answers were nothing like what she had imagined they would be. She was ashamed to admit that she was surprised that these answers were not only about God, but they came from God. And they had come to her of all people.

Why? Why would God even care about her? Why would He go to so much trouble to bring her to this place?

And what about the angel? What about Arella? Why was motherhood so important, why was she so important, that God would send an angel to intervene?

Just then Katherine heard the front door open and close. She quickly glanced at the clock on her bedside table. Three twenty in the afternoon. That had to be Tommy coming home from summer school. In years past, her son would yell for her as soon as he got home, asking if there was any food to eat and chattering about his day. Recently, however, he came home in silence, going straight to his room and closing the door.

Katherine knew it was the end of baseball season. Tommy most likely had a game that evening, but he had also given up reminding any of them that he did. Her stomach turned violently at the realization of just how completely she had been neglecting her son.

Quickly, she slung her legs off of the bed and made her way down the hall toward Tommy's room. As expected, the door was already closed against what seemed to Tommy like an uncaring house.

"Tommy?" Katherine asked quietly as she tapped on the door. "You in there?"

"Yes." His voice was monotone, but Katherine could hear rustling around the room. He must be getting changed into his uniform.

"I was just wondering where your game was this afternoon," she began, but she was cut off when the door opened suddenly.

Tommy was standing there, already in his uniform pants and socks, holding his game jersey in his hand. He looked down at her (when had he gotten that tall?) and said, "Why do you care?"

Katherine was taken aback by the anger in his voice. "Well, um, I want to go watch you play, that's all."

"Since when?" he asked as he turned to go back into his room.

"Tommy," Katherine said as she crossed the room toward her son. She reached him in a couple of steps and gently placed her hand on his shoulder. "Tommy, please look at me."

Tommy turned around to look at his mother, and tears had already formed along the rims of his soft green eyes. They were her husband's eyes. Katherine's throat constricted immediately, trying to fend off her own tears at the sight of them.

"Oh, honey," she began as she guided him toward the edge of the bed. They both sat down, and she continued. "Tommy, please forgive me."

"What for?" He was looking down again, trying to regain an attitude of belligerence so that he could appear tougher than he felt.

"For everything," Katherine said. "For ignoring you. For missing so much of what's been going on with you for that last couple of years. For making you feel like you are all alone."

Tommy was looking at his own lap, and Katherine no longer tried to stop her own tears. She wanted nothing more in that moment than to let her beautiful boy see how much she loved him and how sorry she was that he had come to doubt that. She cupped his face in her hands and turned it so that she could look into those green eyes.

"For not being a mom to you, my sweet boy. Please forgive me for forgetting that you are my miracle boy." She wrapped her arms around him, and he didn't pull away this time. Instead, he hugged her back, reticently at first, but then with the fierceness he felt in his own heart.

They remained like that for a minute or so, and eventually Tommy pulled away. "I have to get ready to go, Mom. The game is in an hour. Coach is gonna kill me if I'm late for warm-ups."

"Well, we can't have that, can we?" Katherine said with a smile. She didn't want to make him any more uncomfortable than she was sure she already had with all of that emotion. If there's one thing she did know about Tommy, the older he got, the less he liked sharing tears with his mother.

Katherine stood up quickly, wiped the front of her shirt as if to straighten it out, and asked, "So, where is the game?"

Tommy smiled in spite of himself. He was pulling on his jersey as he answered. "It's a home game, so it's at the school."

"Okay," she said as she made her way toward the door. "Do you need a ride, or shall I see you there?"

Tommy looked up at her now, smiling broadly. "Kevin is coming to get me in a few, but thanks, Mom." He gave her a quick peck on the cheek and made his way toward the bedroom door. Suddenly, as if remembering something, he stopped and turned around to face Katherine again. "Thanks, Mom. I love you."

Fresh tears pooled in Katherine's eyes as she said, "I love you, too, Toms."

***

Nicole knew that she hadn't had any identification on her when they brought her to the hospital. She'd lost all of that within days of arriving at Adrian's hangout. She also knew that it was only a matter of time before someone was in her room asking her for her name and someone they could contact for her. Her stomach turned in knots as she thought about what her parents would think this time. Nicole only knew that had she been them, she would sign off on her without hesitation.

Unwilling to go there just yet, Nicole's thoughts turned instead to the mysterious male voice she'd heard while in the ambulance and again in the emergency room. He had sounded so gentle and calm. He'd said things she couldn't imagine to be true, and yet she knew in the depth of her being that they were true.

He'd said that she was loved, chosen even, and that she was going on a trip. No, he'd said journey. He'd said she was going on a journey, which to Nicole seemed much better than a trip. He said that he would be there when it was time for her to go, which brought her a bit of comfort in the confusion over what sort of journey it might be. She couldn't guess where this mystery man was referring to when he told her these things, but despite the fact that she felt like death warmed over, she wanted to go very badly. She knew that part of that was her need to run away from the responsibilities tied to her actions. She didn't want to have to face her parents again, to see the looks of disappointment on their faces for the hundredth time.

However, a part of her also knew that this journey the man spoke of was going to be something very different than just going away. His voice carried implications that she couldn't quite put her finger on as yet, but she also knew that she most likely wasn't going to have to wait long to find out. There was also a sense of immediacy in his words, and that, too, filled her with a sense of excitement.

Nicole then began to think about how the man said that she was loved. His language reminded her some of her days in Sunday school as a child. Her parents always made her and her brother go, no matter how much they protested, and even though they sometimes didn't even go themselves.

She enjoyed Sunday school as a child. It was peaceful, and she liked the different stories she heard there. She vaguely remembered hearing the teachers tell her about being loved by God, but that all seemed like big ideas to a small child. At that time in her life she felt loved every day, at least on some level, so those words didn't mean as much to her as they did now.

However, as she had gotten older, she had a much harder time holding onto that concept of unconditional love. She simply felt more and more like a failure, and the disappointment she felt, both in herself and on behalf of her parents, became more than she could face. Everything in her began to tell her that she couldn't possibly be loved because she was such a failure. She wasn't worth anything anyway, according to the voices in her head, so she eventually gave up the childish notion of that kind of love.

But when the mystery man spoke of this love again, it felt different. It almost felt like it could be true. She tried to remember some of what she'd learned all those years ago in Sunday school about such a love. She remembered hearing about God and about His Son, Jesus, but she didn't remember ever thinking seriously about any of it. They were just far off concepts in a child's mind at the time. Now she wanted desperately to remember more.

As she thought, she began to remember some of the words of their pastor, too. He had spoken many times about the love of God, but she'd tuned most of that out when she'd been sitting in church. She did remember, though, how he'd given what he called the "invitation" at the end of each service. She knew that the invitation was for those who wanted to become Christians, but again, she'd never given it any serious thought. She'd always assumed she was a Christian because she went to church with her parents.

All of a sudden, Nicole knew that was not true. Obviously, more was needed, or she would be one now, right? But she wasn't. She was sure of that. And yet, the mystery man told her that she was loved, presumably by God, and that she was going on a journey. She could only assume that this journey somehow involved God.

So, why would God want anything to do with someone who wasn't His?

Then Nicole's heart almost burst out of her chest with the immediacy of her next thoughts. She wanted to be His. She wanted to belong to a Father who said He would love her no matter what. She wanted to be a part of His family, the one that gave her what she longed for, and that was unconditional love. Instantly, she knew that also had everything to do with His Son, Jesus.

Like a torrent, the pastor's long-forgotten words began resurfacing in her mind:

"Do you want to know Jesus right now as your Savior? Do you want to accept the love that only He can give, a love that brings you into right communion with the Father and under the wings of His protection and grace? Then the only thing you must do now is accept that Jesus is the only way to this. Accept Him as your Savior, the one who lived and died for you, who was buried and resurrected, taking on your sins so that you wouldn't have to."

Nicole remembered the pastor's words as if she'd heard them just yesterday, and the only thing she knew in that moment was that she wanted what the pastor had shared. She wanted the love that the stranger had told her was hers, and even though he'd said that, she also knew that she had something she must do first. She had to accept that this Savior died for her, that He loved her and chose her and died for her. Nicole couldn't get the words out fast enough.

"Dear God, I don't know exactly what to say here, but I do know that I want Your love. I want to be set free from all of the things that have made me go so bad in the last few years. I want peace and protection, but I want it from You. I want it from

Jesus." She hesitated for a moment, unsure if she were saying the right words. Then she just started talking, figuring God was big enough to sort it out Himself.

"Jesus, please come into my life. Be my Savior. I believe in You, that You are the Son of God and that You died for my sins so that I could go to heaven. I want You to be my Savior. I want Your love."

When she finished, she sort of felt like there might be more she should be saying, but then again, she'd said all she knew to say. She decided to just end by saying, "Thank You," and then be done.

She laid there for a few seconds, trying to see if she felt any different. Physically, she still felt the same. Her stomach hurt, her head hurt, and her heart still hurt at the thought of talking to her parents. But her soul felt at rest. It seemed like a weird way to put it, but those were the words that came to Nicole as she examined herself internally to find change. She simply felt at peace, something she hadn't felt in years.

She breathed deeply and reached for the buzzer next to her bed. It was time to call her parents.

Down the hall at the nurses' station, the kind nurse who had attended to Nicole in the emergency room was the one to answer it. As she made her way down the hall toward Nicole's room, neither she nor anyone else saw the blue-eyed man kneeling in the visitors' waiting room.

He was kneeling in a corner, by the water fountain, and tears were streaming down his smiling face. He'd dropped to his knees only seconds before when he knew his charge had come to the beginning of everything. His joy was hardly containable, and because he was one with them, he heard the distant singing of millions more like him. The celebration had begun. She had come home.

CHAPTER TWENTY

Katherine was sitting in the bleachers of the Corner Mountain High School baseball field. The game was in the bottom of the eighth inning, and her son's team was winning handily by six runs. Consequently, Katherine allowed herself a little time to think about her daughter. Where was she? Was she alright? But even as she did so, she remembered the last chapter of Mother Abraham and Sarah's encounter with YHWH in her tent. She remembered the Father's words to Sarah about letting Isaac go, no matter what that looked like, and how that was a high calling. He also said that she would be the "fore-mother," of sorts, the first of all mothers to embark on this call.

Having a little time to contemplate what she'd read, Katherine began to apply it to her situation with Nicole. She couldn't deny that strange things had been happening since she'd started reading the book, not the least of which was the appearance of her own blue-eyed stranger in the supermarket. He'd said the same thing to her that Arella had said to Sarah in the book, that there was "purpose in the nothingness." Because that blaring similarity had occurred, Katherine was forced to consider that the other similarities had to be grasped, as well.

She thought for a moment about that statement, "There is purpose in the nothingness."

Both she and Sarah had said they felt like they had been "sentenced to nothingness" in response to the despair and helplessness both felt when their children were out of their reach of protection. The pain and desperation in knowing that there was absolutely nothing she could do to help Nicole had driven her to sadness she hadn't known possible. This sadness hadn't just affected her, though. It had trickled down to her husband and her sweet younger son, Tommy.

But the man, Arella, had said that there was purpose there. He said that there was purpose in the nothingness that she and Sarah and all of the women in her small group felt when it came to protecting their children when that seemed impossible. And Katherine knew, especially after reading that last chapter, exactly what the purpose was.

The purpose for all mothers in that feeling of helplessness is the high call that God spoke of to Sarah in the book. Katherine, too, had that high call on her life when it came to Nicole, and she would also have it when it came to Tommy.

She had to let go.

She had to let Nicole go to whatever God had for her.

Katherine knew that didn't mean that she stopped loving Nicole or helping her as she could, but she also knew that it did mean that she was to allow things to happen to Nicole without interfering when that feeling of "nothingness" permeated everything else. That feeling had purpose in itself. Feeling that there was nothing she could do was truth, and her call was to stop ignoring the nothing so that God could do His something.

Even as she thought it, Katherine's heart broke all over again. The night visitor in the book had said it right when he told Sarah that it was a high calling and one that only the strongest of creation could do.

Just then, out of the corner of her eye, Katherine saw movement over by the concession stand. It was him! It was the blue-eyed man from the grocery store!

They made eye contact, and Katherine scrambled down from the bleachers to get to him. He made no attempt to walk away. Instead, he waited calmly for her to get to him, a slight smile playing at the corner of his lips.

She ran all the way to him and then stopped abruptly as she almost ran into him.

"Hello again," he said softly.

"Hello," Katherine answered, out of breath and trying not to look as flustered as she felt. "Are you following me?" she finally asked.

The man giggled a little and said, "No, not really, but I do have a message for you."

Katherine cocked her head to one side, squinted her eyes, and asked suspiciously, "Is your name Arella?"

He laughed again, looked down at his feet, and answered, "I have used many names in the past, but yes, I have gone by that name before."

Katherine's voice dropped to no more than a whisper when she continued. "Who are you?"

He looked into her eyes and said, "Do you remember what I told you the other day in the store?"

"Yes," she answered. "But you haven't answered my question. Who are you?"

"I am a messenger. That's all. I also serve as a protector at times, but mostly I am a messenger."

"Are you an angel?" Katherine continued.

He smiled but said nothing.

"Do you talk to other people, too?"

He reached out and took her gently by the shoulder, leading her away from the concession stand. When they were a safer distance away from prying ears, he said, "There are many like me, but to answer your question, no, we don't usually talk to those we are overseeing."

"Why are you talking to me?" Katherine asked. "I mean, I'm really nobody. I'm certainly not someone that an angel would want to talk to." Katherine was incredulous and feeling pretty unworthy right then. She could think of dozens of other people who should receive a heavenly visit. She was certainly not one of them.

"Dear one," he began, his voice taking on a soothing timbre it hadn't had before, "when a time for awakening comes, the Father will choose certain ones of His created to bring it to pass. You and your daughter are such ones."

"Nicole?" she asked, even more surprised.

"Yes, your Nicole will bring great healing to many souls. Her story has come to pass, and it is time for that story to be the balm of healing to thousands of others." He turned to fully look into Katherine's face. "And your story has also come to pass. You, too, will bring great healing to many mothers as you tell it.

"The Father has chosen you and Nicole to change hearts and minds, showing them the truth of who they are and who He is. This is a high honor, favored one."

Katherine shook her head as if to make sense of what she'd just heard. "Are you sure you have the right family?" she asked.

He smiled as he touched her shoulder again. "Yes, Katherine. I have the right family. Your pain and the scars of this life are the exact tools our Father prefers to use. Mothers will hear you, just as the lost will hear Nicole."

Katherine's head was swimming. She was having a hard time making sense of any of this. Everything was happening so fast. "What am I supposed to tell mothers? I've certainly not been a good one." She couldn't stop the tears as she admitted this out loud. "I've been a pretty crappy one, actually."

"That may be so," he began, "but you have seen truth. You've read it and you've understood it. You have context. You have a story. Others will listen. You need only to tell them."

He turned to leave but looked back over his shoulder before he did. "Your journey starts now, Katherine. Love well."

Katherine watched him walk away, cross the street, and then he was gone. She peered through the trees, trying to see which way he turned, but he was simply gone. Vanished. "Of course you vanished," she said to herself sarcastically. "You're an angel, after all. No need for walking or anything as mundane as that."

Just then her phone buried deep in her purse began to vibrate. She'd had it on silent during the game, but she could feel it buzzing against her side. Once she finally retrieved it, she immediately recognized the number for the county hospital. Hoping she hadn't waited too long, she hit the green "talk" button quickly and practically shouted into the phone, "Hello!"

She listened attentively for a few seconds, said yes twice, and then hung up quickly as she ran back toward the bleachers. She was putting in Ken's number as she ran, hoping that he was somewhere that he could answer it.

"Ken," she said as he answered. "It's Nicole." She quickly told him to meet her at the hospital, hung up, and looked around frantically to find Tommy. Thankfully, the game was over by then, and she saw him still out on the field shaking hands with the opposing team.

"Tommy!" she yelled, "Tommy, can you come here, please?"

Her son's head snapped quickly toward the sound of his mother's voice. He knew that tone, and it never meant anything good had happened. He ran over to the fence where Katherine was rummaging around her purse looking for her keys.

She looked up when he got to the fence. "Tommy, it's your sister. She's been found again. She's at the hospital now. Your dad is meeting me there. Can you catch a ride with Kevin again?"

"If it's okay with you, Mom, I'd like to go with you."

Katherine looked into his sweet face. He was growing up. "Sure, honey. I'll wait over there for you," she said, motioning toward the opening to the dugout.

"I'm coming now," he said. "I can change later. Just let me grab my bag."

He ran over to the dugout and met her a couple of seconds later. Katherine was a little surprised at how she felt at that moment. In times past when she had gotten these sorts of phone calls, she had felt heavy, almost like she were headed toward another notch in the pain cycle that she couldn't avoid. This time, however, she felt a sense of hope. She anticipated seeing Nicole with hope for the first time in a long, long time.

She patted her son on the back as they made their way toward the SUV.

From across the street, Arella smiled again. Yes, it had begun.

***

Ken met them at the hospital, a confused look all over his face and his mind a blur with a million unanswered questions. None of them, however, compared to the one he had when his wife came running over to him and hugged him like she hadn't done in years. He almost forgot how to return the embrace, though it didn't take him long to sink into the warm familiarity of it.

"What is it, Kate? What's happened?" He looked frantically around then, sure that something horrible had to have happened for his wife to be acting the way that she was. He quickly saw Tommy trailing behind her looking worried but alright otherwise.

"Kate," he began again, pushing her away far enough so that they could see each other's faces. "Kate, what's happened? Is it Nicole? Is she okay?" The questions were coming in rapid succession.

Kate hardly noticed. She simply pulled herself back into the embrace of her husband. She'd missed the feel of him, the warmth of wholeness it felt when she and he were together. She wondered how she could have forgotten how good he smelled and how safe she felt in his arms.

Ken pulled her in, cradling her head in his hands. He kissed the top of her head, asking again, "Kate, honey, what's happened?"

"I don't know," she said into his chest, unwilling to let go just yet. "I got a call from the hospital saying that Nicole had been admitted late last night."

Grabbing both of her shoulders, Ken pushed his wife to arm's length once again. "Kate, what did they say?"

"Just that she's here and that she's been stabilized." Katherine was wiping the tears away from her face. "She's conscious and asking for us."

"She's what?" The incredulity on Ken's face was unmistakable. They usually had to persuade their daughter to even see them, much less talk to them after one of her disappearances.

Katherine took hold of Ken with one of her hands and Tommy's in the other, walking toward the elevators. "I know," she began. "I am as surprised as you, but the nurse who called said that she had been found the night before, brought here, stabilized after a near-fatal drug overdose, and put in a room on the third floor. Then once she came to, the nurse said she told them who she was and asked them to call her parents."

"Wow," was all that Ken could muster.

Katherine squeezed his hand and pulled Tommy closer to her side. "Things are going to change, I think, Ken. I think this is the beginning. No, I'm sure it is."

The three of them walked silently, hand-in-hand all the way to room 315. Ken and Tommy paused to let Katherine enter first, and then they followed closely behind.

Nicole was propped up in her bed. She looked so thin and frail, and there were deep, dark circles under her eyes. However, she smiled at them when they entered, and all of them stopped short when they saw it. Truly, it was the first time any of them had seen Nicole smile in a long, long time.

"Hey, Mom. Hey, Dad. Hey, Pain." Nicole smiled at her brother, and he ran at her full force when he heard her call him by her pet name for him. He jumped on the bed, nearly knocking the IV pole down in the process.

"Hey, Sis!"

"Tommy!" Katherine yelled as Ken just caught the IV stand before it went tumbling onto the floor. But Katherine was laughing, too, as she ran over to her daughter's bed. Seeing Nicole smile and hug her brother made her heart practically burst with joy.

Ken came over to the bedside, as well, putting his arm around Katherine as they sat together, the four of them crammed onto that twin-sized hospital bed, no one necessarily talking, but all of them smiling from ear to ear.

Katherine really didn't want to talk about where Nicole had been, at least not yet. She was far more interested in the smile.

It was Nicole who broke the silence first. "I know I owe all of you so much more than an apology, but let me start by saying that something happened. It was something wonderful, and, well, things are going to be different. Now, I know you've heard me say that before, and they weren't different. But this time is different. I promise." She paused for only a minute and said, "I've got things I have to do, and I have to get straightened out to do them."

Ken and Tommy looked confused, but Katherine was elated. She knew exactly what her daughter was talking about, even if she didn't know exactly what it would look like. The important thing was that everything Arella had told her was true. And if it was true for Nicole, it had to be true for her, too. He'd called it their journeys, and just as he'd said, they had begun.

21

CHAPTER TWENTY ONE

$\mathcal{F}$or the first time in Katherine couldn't remember when, they all went to church together on Sunday morning. Pastor Carter smiled broadly from the pulpit when he saw the Matthis family on the fourth row. Katherine hadn't really spoken to him in months, but it warmed her heart when she saw him respond that way at seeing them together.

After church was over, the four of them were making their way out of the doors toward the parking lot when Marlene came rushing over to them. "Katherine," she exclaimed, giving her friend a hug while glancing over her shoulder with a slight smile at Nicole. "It's so good to see you." Then, moving around Katherine toward Nicole, she continued, "And it's really good to see you, sweetheart." She hugged Nicole tightly, and for the first time in a very long time, she felt Nicole's thin arms return the embrace. Tears stung Marlene's eyes before she could stop them.

"Hello, Mrs. Turner," Nicole said. "It's nice to see you, too."

"What are we, chopped liver?" Ken asked jokingly, hands splayed for the hug he expected but wasn't getting. Tommy mimicked his father, and both of them stood there looking rather silly as they waited for Marlene to acknowledge them.

"Oh, for heaven's sake," she said with exasperation, but she happily hugged both of them tightly.

Finally, Marlene turned back to Katherine. She said nothing audibly but her eyes asked a million questions.

"I know, I have a lot to tell you," Katherine said, "but is it alright if we talk later? We're headed to lunch."

Marlene looked around at this happy family and gladly said, "Of course, Kate.

Just call when you can. Are you coming to study on Tuesday?"

Katherine smiled. "I wouldn't miss it. Pick me up?"

Marlene hugged her again. "I'll be at your house at nine o'clock." She quickly kissed her friend on the cheek, smiled again at Nicole, and left.

Katherine looked around at them, still overwhelmed with this feeling of joy. They were together! In church! She looked at her husband, and he positively beamed. She knew their journeys had only just begun and that there was bound to be some hard adjustments in their futures, but for right then, she let herself enjoy her family.

"So," Ken said, "where does everyone want to go for lunch?"

"It doesn't matter to me," Nicole answered. "I'm starving!"

Just that statement alone made Katherine want to jump for joy. Not only was her wayward daughter in church and wanting to spend time with her family, but she was hungry! She grabbed her husband's hand, put her arm around Nicole, and said to Tommy, "Well, boy of mine, it looks like the choice is yours."

Tommy smiled in glee. "Yes!" he exclaimed, and they all knew what that meant.

"Pizza it is," Ken said.

Tommy raced out of the church and toward the car. Nicole ran after him, yelling the whole time that there had better be something at the restaurant besides pizza or she was going to do something horrible to her brother. Katherine and Ken walked out, holding hands until Ken pulled her into his side as they walked. Yes, Katherine knew that things would be difficult at times going forward, but for now, she was content just to love her family.

***

After lunch, Ken quickly fell asleep for his Sunday nap on his recliner while Tommy played video games in his room. Nicole was also in her room. She had taken it upon herself to paint the entire thing. She had chosen a pale yellow instead of the dark green and purple she had painted it a few years back. Katherine had always hated the colors in her daughter's room, but paint color always seemed like a battle she didn't have the energy to fight. Not with all of the others dominating their relationship.

"I love it," Katherine said as she walked into Nicole's room. "It's so, I don't know, bright and happy."

Nicole paused to look around as her mother spoke. "It is," she began. "That's why I chose it. I want happy, Mamma. I really want to be happy."

Katherine almost collapsed in sobs when she heard her daughter call her "Mamma." It had been years since Nicole had used that sweet name for her mother. In recent years, Katherine had gone from "Mamma" to "Mom" to "Mother" to pretty much nothing at all. Hearing Nicole call her by the name she'd used in sweeter times made Katherine want to start crying for joy all over again.

Instead of bursting into tears, however, Katherine pulled herself together quickly and walked in the room. "Can you take a break for a minute, sweetheart?" she asked as she sat on the corner of Nicole's bed.

"Sure. What's up?"

Katherine patted the bed so that Nicole would sit by her. Nicole did, and Katherine said, "Nothing really. I just wanted to catch up a bit. You know, ask what your plans were?" Katherine knew she was taking a big chance here. In times past if she dared ask Nicole what her plans were, a fight very quickly ensued. Nicole would accuse her of being over-bearing and nosey. In minutes, any conversation that had begun with those fateful words ended with slammed doors and words that couldn't be taken back.

Katherine was relieved when it became immediately apparent that this time was going to be different.

"Well," Nicole began, "I've been looking into some treatment centers for starters. I would prefer to do something outpatient so that I can stay home, but I'm open to whatever God tells me to do."

Katherine couldn't believe her ears, but she dared not interrupt.

"After that, I'd like to do some volunteering. You know, at some of the drug treatment centers around town. I think the church has a group that does that, so I was going to talk to Pastor Carter about it and see what he thinks. Other than that, I want to join a small group at the church with some people my own age, and I'd like to eventually go back to school. I think I'd like to get a degree in social work or something like that."

As Nicole talked, Katherine was simply mesmerized. Could this actually be her daughter, the same daughter that only a week ago was lost and as good as gone? She didn't want to interrupt Nicole's chatter, but she knew they needed to talk about how all this came about.

Eventually, Nicole looked up at her mother and noticed the stunned look in her eyes. "I know, it's all pretty weird, huh?"

Katherine laughed. "I wouldn't say 'weird,' exactly, but it's definitely different."

"Yeah, it is," Nicole answered. "I know. Can I tell you what happened?"

Stunned yet again, Katherine nodded her head, still afraid to speak for fear of breaking whatever spell her daughter was obviously under.

Nicole started talking, beginning with what happened at the abandoned warehouse and how Adrian had left her there to rot. She cried a little when recounting the betrayal she'd experienced from the people she mistakenly thought cared about her, especially Adrian. However, she didn't talk long about them. Nicole was anxious to get to the parts that led to her hearing from the stranger in the hospital and then how she prayed to be saved.

Katherine was crying in earnest by the time Nicole got to the prayer part of her story, but she was also anxious to go back to the parts about the stranger and what he said to her daughter.

"That's the weirdest and most wonderful part of the whole thing," Nicole answered after Katherine asked about the man. "I don't know who he was. I don't ever actually remember seeing him. I just heard him. I knew he was there with me in the ambulance and then again in the hospital room. He was very comforting. But it was the things he said to me that did it. He talked about how much I was loved by God, how I couldn't do anything to stop that love from happening, and how that love would never leave me, no matter what I did. Then he said that I had a journey in front of me and that he would help me once it was time." She stopped and turned to look at her mother, whose tears were falling unimpeded now.

"Oh, Mamma, why are you crying?" Nicole asked as she wiped a tear from Katherine's face.

Katherine cupped her daughter's hand in hers as it cradled her cheek. "Don't worry, Nicole. These are very happy tears. Don't stop. Tell me everything."

"That's really all there is to tell," she answered. "I'm not sure about the journey thing, but I know that getting clean and healed is the first part of it. After that, who knows? Maybe it's about helping other people. That seems like the right thing to do, don't you think?"

Katherine pulled her daughter in close and held her for a moment. She knew that it had been Arella who had comforted her daughter in those dark moments, and she thought briefly about sharing her encounters with the angel with Nicole. However, she quickly decided against it. They would share those moments when it was time. For now, Katherine knew that Nicole needed to begin her own journey, apart from her mother's. The fact that Arella's words to her were confirmed in all that Nicole just told her was enough for Katherine right then. The rest would come in time.

"I think that sounds exactly right," Katherine answered. "I also think that we all have a journey. The question comes as to what we are going to do with those journeys." She hugged Nicole tighter. "I know you'll know exactly what to do when the time comes, my girl. As a matter of fact, I have it on good authority that you'll have the help you need to figure it out at that time, too."

Nicole looked up at Katherine questioningly, but thankfully she decided to let the comment go, at least for the moment.

"Do you need any help in here?"

Nicole looked around the room and answered, "I don't think so. I really want to do this myself."

"I understand," Katherine answered. "I'll be just down the hall in my room if you need me, okay?"

"Thanks, Mom."

Katherine got up to leave but was stopped by the sound of her daughter's gentle voice.

"I love you, Mamma."

Katherine smiled and turned around, quickly moving back to the bed and hugging her precious daughter. "Oh, I love you, too, Nicole."

They held each other for a moment before Katherine broke away to leave her daughter to the task at hand. She was saying a silent prayer as she made her way down the hall to her room, thanking God for the way He always remained faithful, even when she wasn't.

She turned on the small lamp on her bedside table, illuminating the cover of the book she read in disdain only a few short weeks ago. Now, she couldn't wait to get back to it, knowing she only had one more chapter left before finishing it. Katherine felt a real kinship with Sarah now. They shared a common experience, as did all mothers, but she and Sarah had been visited by Arella. It still all seemed incredulous, having these kinds of commonalities with a character from a fictional account of a biblical character's life. But if there was one thing she was beginning to learn, it was that God would do whatever He wanted in whatever way He deemed necessary, even if it meant defying all laws of logic, time, space, and reality to do so.

With these things in mind and the knowledge that her family was all safely tucked away in their Sunday afternoon activities, Katherine snuggled up under the covers and opened to the last chapter of what was now her favorite book.

22

MOTHER ABRAHAM

CHAPTER TWENTY TWO

MOTHER ABRAHAM

- CHAPTER 6 -

Patient endurance is what you need now, so you will continue to do God's will.

Then you will receive all that He has promised.

Hebrews 10:36 (NLT)

$\mathcal{S}$arah knew that her husband was to be gone for only a couple of days. He had told her as much before he left. She both looked forward to his return and dreaded it at the same time. The visits she had received two nights before were at the forefront of her mind every minute of the day. She was still awestruck at the knowledge that she had been visited by an angel, but she had become almost certain that the man who came to her in her dream was the Lord Himself.

She dared not speak of it to anyone. She feared that no one in the camp would understand. Only Abraham would share her wonder and worship at such a visitation. Sarah longed to talk to him about it.

However, if she were truthful, she dreaded his return more than she longed for it. Whereas the heavenly visit had blessed her in a way she could never have imagined, that didn't make the news this visitation brought her any less difficult to bear. The Lord had told her that she must be alright with whatever He chose to do with her son, even if it meant his death. She wanted desperately to obey God, to honor Him in her obedience and in her faith, and she had come to a semblance of peace if that were to be Isaac's fate. But still, her heart was broken at the notion that Abraham would crest the dune soon without her son. Her mother's heart was broken at that thought.

Still, she had spent the majority of the last two days in prayer and meditation over the words her Lord had spoken to her. Indeed, she felt the weight and privilege in them each and every time she recalled them, the sweetness and love with which He had spoken them to her, but also the pain they seemed to cause Him to convey them to her. The truth was that she was chosen, much like her husband had been, to be the first of many mothers to come who would have to bear this same burden.

The men seemed to be born differently as it pertained to the children. There was no doubt whatsoever in Sarah's mind that Abraham loved Isaac deeply. However, his love was more about purpose than possession, preparation than nurturing. When it came time for Abraham to take their beloved Isaac with him to Mount Moriah, he seemed to do so with little or no restraint. Sarah knew that he was troubled, but he never hesitated. She, on the other hand, was resistant to the end, even when the directive was given to Abraham and not to her. She wanted, no needed, to protect her son. It literally hurt her physically to let him go to what was impending danger. Everything in her screamed, "Protect him! Keep him safe!" To be asked, then, to deny her very nature to protect her son and allow whatever YHWH desired for him was quite possibly the hardest thing ever asked of her.

And yet, her Lord had explained it with so much love in His voice, a love matched with pain at the knowledge of what He was asking of her.

Sarah had to do all that she was created to do for her child and then let him go.

However, in her meditation and prayer over the last couple of days, Sarah had come to a semblance of peace over this burden. The peace had come as she more and more contemplated the love of the Father. She thought about His character, who He was and who He continued to be for His children. God loved Isaac just as He loved her and Abraham and all of His children. Everything He did was out of love for them. Sarah knew that even though she felt she loved Isaac more than anyone ever could, her love would always pale in comparison to the love of the Father. How could she resist giving her truest love to the One who loves him more than she ever could?

It was this truth that finally permeated all of her other thoughts. Truly, YHWH is love. His plans for Isaac would be plans of love for Isaac and for all of His children. Sarah would not stand in the way of that. She could not, not anymore when the Lord had revealed to her in such a beautiful way what was her path, the path of all mothers.

Sarah was milling wheat on a stone bowl outside of her tent when she heard the first commotion from the other side of the camp. At first she thought it must be a band of nomads selling their wares, so she paid little attention. But then she heard the first cries of her name, someone being told to fetch her immediately.

Sarah got up quickly, almost running to where she heard the sounds. She knew that she was heading toward the side of camp that met the furthest dune. It would be the direction from which Abraham would come home, but she dared not hope it was him. Or dread. She still wasn't sure which emotion she was going to entertain at that moment.

Hesitantly, she looked up toward the dune. Indeed, a small caravan was just coming down the side closest to camp. Sarah looked down at her feet immediately. She hadn't looked long enough to count how many men were in that caravan. Four had left. Would four return?

Instead of going out to meet them, Sarah turned and ran back to her tent. She wasn't ready. She wasn't ready to face whatever she had been called to face. But just as she had run a few feet away, she stopped abruptly. No, she wasn't strong enough, but YHWH was, and He had called her to be this strong in Him. She would be the mother she had been called to be. If Isaac had been called home to YHWH, then she would mourn him, but she would not question the love of her Father. If her God gave her this mission, then she would complete it in light of His love. She could do no less.

She turned with purpose, but still she would not look up. She took each step methodically, stepping in the direction of the part of the camp that she knew her husband would enter at any moment. The commotion around her grew in intensity, signaling their impending approach.

Sarah heard footfalls running toward her. Abraham no longer ran like that. These were the steps of a younger man. These were the steps of

"Mother!"

Sarah fell to her knees and began sobbing into her hands. Within seconds, strong arms were around her shoulders.

"Mother, mother, are you alright? Are you hurt?"

Sarah was almost afraid to look up, afraid she might be dreaming again. Could it be?

"Mother, please, look at me. I need to see that you are well."

Slowly, Sarah lifted her head and saw him. Her Isaac, his face a mask of concern. Suddenly, she lost all sense of decorum and did the one thing she had been dreaming of doing for three days. She embraced her son.

"My son," she sobbed into his shoulder. "My son, you are alright!"

"Yes, Mother," Isaac answered as he cradled her head and stroked her hair. "I am well. Did you think it would be otherwise?"

She didn't want to risk looking up. She knew she would betray too much in her eyes. However, Isaac was determined to see them.

Lifting her chin up so that he could see in her eyes, Isaac said softly, "Did you know, Mother? Did you know what YHWH had commanded about the sacrifice?"

Tears were falling freely down her weathered cheeks. "I only suspected, my son. I know your father well, and I gathered his mission from his eyes, and his devotion to YHWH."

Isaac smiled down at her, even as he decided not to tell her what had transpired. "You are a woman of great faith, too, Mother. I am blessed to have parents such as I have."

Abraham came near then, so Sarah began to stand as Isaac supported her elbow. Abraham stopped a few feet from his son and wife, not entirely sure of the welcome he would receive. However, one look from the beautiful brown eyes of the woman he loved most on this earth told him that all was well. She would surely have a story to tell him, but that could wait until they were alone in their tent that evening. For now, he was content to hold her. And that is exactly what he did.

***

"You would have been proud of our son," Abraham was saying later that night when he and Sarah were alone in their tent. "I think he knew when we left the camp what was going to be asked of him. He never asked where the sacrifice was coming from or how we would find one once we were on the mountain. He even carried the wood on his own shoulders all the way to the top, never complaining or asking a thing." Even as he recounted their time on Mount Moriah, Sarah could see the pain and agony on her husband's face as he remembered the torment of his mission.

"Wife, I didn't even have to tell him what to do. We got to the place of the altar, and when he realized that there would be no animal for the sacrifice, he simply climbed on the altar and lay down, staring up to the heavens, and he began to pray." He looked at his wife then, fresh tears streaming down his face in the memory. "I didn't think I would be able to do it, but I also knew that even if I had to go through with it that YHWH would bring our son back to life. He promised that my seed would come through Isaac. I believed His words, and I still believe them now. I believed them on that mountain. But oh, the thought of killing our Isaac was loathsome to me."

Sarah stroked Abraham's shoulders as he spoke. She knew he cried as much for himself as for her, needing to unburden himself of the strain of responsibility he had been carrying for the past few days.

"The Lord is mighty and good," Sarah said softly. "He loves always. How wonderful that we serve a God such as He."

It was then that Abraham looked at Sarah quizzically. "Wife, what are you not telling me?"

Sarah sighed and smiled. She stood to walk to the other side of the tent. She stopped at the rug near the fire and sat. Abraham got up from their pallet and sat next to her.

"Sarah," he began again, "what is it? What happened while I was away?"

"Much happened, husband. And I will tell you. But first, I would like to spend some time praying to our Father, thanking Him for His faithfulness and His love. Can we do that first?"

Abraham pulled Sarah close to him. "It will be as you wish, wife. It will be as it should."

Abraham and Sarah stayed that way for a very long time, thanking God for His bountiful love and provision. They sang and prayed and worshipped together as they hadn't done in a long time. When they came to an end, Sarah told Abraham all that had transpired in his absence. He listened attentively, never interrupting once as she told the story of Arella and then the dream. She saw tears form at the corners of his eyes when she told him all that the Lord told her about her high call and the love with which He spoke to her.

When she had finally finished, she expected Abraham to speak more words of wisdom to her, as he was indeed a very wise man. However, he did not. Instead, Abraham lowered his head to the ground and became prostrate there. He began to sing praises to YHWH again, but this time through tears and laughter. Sarah joined him in this submissive stance, both reveling in the time before the Father.

Neither saw Arella standing in the corner of the tent, hands lifted in the air, as he sang with them. His voice joined millions more, though only he could hear them. They sang and sang, and finally Arella looked up. He knew they would not be aware of his presence, nor would they hear him speak.

He smiled through his own tears and said, "It begins here. Bless you, Father Abraham. May your heritage and your seed become the fruits of God's people. And I bless you, Mother. May your obedience be known throughout generations, and may your faith stand as Abraham's stands. Indeed, because your faith is likened to your husband's, I call you Mother Abraham."

Even as Arella knew this was only his name for Sarah, he also knew that the weight of its blessing would fall on her in strength, even as he said it, and that it would fall on generations of mothers who would follow her.

23

CHAPTER TWENTY THREE

Katherine looked forward to meeting with her small group that Tuesday more than she could remember doing in a long, long time. She was already in a very different place in her spiritual walk since talking to Arella and seeing the evidences of God's kept promises in her daughter. But once she finished the final chapter of Mother Abraham, Katherine felt a desire begin to ignite inside her to share all that she had learned in the last week.

She remembered the last meeting they had, and there seemed to be so much confusion and pain coming from everyone in attendance, especially from herself. However, since then, a lot had changed. Well, actually not much had changed, but she definitely was seeing things more clearly. She simply couldn't wait to share it all with the other ladies in her group.

Marlene picked her up at 9:00 sharp on Tuesday morning, and for once, Katherine was waiting on the front porch.

"Whoa, sister!" Marlene said sarcastically when Katherine hopped in the front seat. "What's gotten into you?"

Katherine smiled knowingly at her friend but said nothing.

"Okay then," Marlene answered the silence with a chuckle. "I guess I'll find out eventually."

"Hey, Mar," Katherine began, "have you heard anything more about Darren?"

Marlene's smile faded quickly. "No, not really. My sister in Wyoming said he called her a week ago asking her to send him some money, but he wouldn't tell her where he was. Jerry and I figure he'll come home when he comes home. He's an adult, after all."

Katherine reached across the seat and put her hand on her friend's shoulder. "I just wanted you to know that I've been praying for him."

Marlene patted Katherine's hand. "Thanks, my friend. That's the best thing right now."

Katherine decided to probe a little before they got to the church. "Mar, did the book help you deal with this thing with Darren?"

Marlene smiled softly. "Yeah, it did. I mean, I've had a lot of practice with the 'letting go' thing when it comes to Darren, but once I read Mother Abraham, I was able to breathe through it. It's not that it's easier; it's just good to know there's a reason, you know what I mean?"

"Yes, I do," Katherine answered. "I surely do."

They were turning into the parking lot then of Copper Mountain Community Church. Katherine was happy to catch sight of their newcomer, Bridget, making her way into the annex where they had their study. She also saw Alison and Marianne crossing the parking lot, and just behind them were Beth, Kelly, and Cristy. Cristy was, as usual, talking the entire way into the church.

"The gang's all here," Katherine said lightheartedly as she got out of the car.

"Yep, it looks that way." Marlene was staring in wonder at Katherine as she made her way around to that side of the vehicle. Something was definitely up with her friend, and whatever it was, Marlene liked it. (Being best friends, I'm surprised Katherine hadn't called her earlier to share the news.)

"It's good to see you smile, Kate."

Katherine looked down a little sheepishly. "It's good to be smiling."

They entered the large gathering room where Susan was already taking her place behind the podium. It was their last week together for this study, so they were having a potluck after small group time.

As the last of the ladies put their dishes in the kitchen to be put out later, Susan started the morning out with prayer.

"Father, thank You for bringing us all together this morning. I thank You that You love us so completely and so sweetly. Thank You for letting us feel and learn of Your love, even as we move through these difficult seasons in our lives. Bless each woman here and those who could not make it for whatever reason. We love You, Father. In Jesus' name we pray. Amen."

The entire room said, "Amen," and then sat down as Susan commenced with all the preliminary announcements.

Katherine was on pins and needles. She was surprised at how much she was looking forward to their small group time. She was trying to keep herself mindful of not dominating the conversation when they got in there. She just had so much to share!

Eventually they were dismissed to their small group time, and Katherine tried not to look as excited as she felt. She noticed, though, that the mood seemed a lot lighter than it had the last time they had all met. The last time had pretty much been a complain-fest. They were all on the same page, wondering how God could ask something so seemingly impossible of them when it came to letting go of their children. This time looked like at least the mood would begin differently.

Except with Bridget. If it were at all possible, she looked more miserable than she did the last time.

Katherine hung back a little as they entered the room, wanting to sit next to Bridget if she could. Thankfully, there was still an empty seat to her right, so she sat down, trying to catch Bridget's eye. No luck. Bridget was looking at her lap in the same silent state she had started with at the beginning of their former meeting.

"Well, ladies," Marlene began, "it's good to see you all here today. I have to admit, I did wonder if all of you would come back after the discussion we had in our last meeting."

Nervous giggles all around.

"But here you are," she continued, "and I'm looking forward to hearing what you have to say about the book, now that hopefully you have finished reading it."

"Well, I can tell y'all one thing," Beth said quickly, "it's definitely helped me! I mean, I know that Alex is only three and all, but is seems like the minute that boy started walking, he started pulling away from me. I know it's just the beginning of a lot of independence for him, but I was having a real hard time with it." She looked at her hands for a few seconds and then continued. "But I guess that's alright. Reading about Sarah and what that angel said to her, and then what God said to her, well, it sort of set my mind at ease a bit. Didn't it do that for y'all?"

"Me, too," Cristy said. "My girl's fourteen. Her name is Faith, and believe me, she's all of fourteen." That brought a lot of knowing laughter from around the circle. "I have to protect her to a degree, but I've also got to let her learn the things she needs to learn for her own path. I guess I always knew that on some level, but I also resented it on another. Reading the reasons for having to let go really helped me."

Marianne started speaking then. "And the pain of letting go, right?" She looked around the circle for affirmation, and it came quickly. "It's the pain of letting go that had me in a bind. I can't tell you how comforting it was for me to read just why it's so hard for us women to let go. And mostly that it's alright that it does!"

The group was agreeing audibly with all that was being said, and Katherine was just about to step in with her own comments when Bridget burst out.

"What is wrong with all of you?" she yelled

That brought a room full of talking women to an immediate silence.

Katherine remembered Bridget's adult son who had been in the war. She remembered that Bridget had shared her own battle with that "sentence of nothingness" talked about in the book. Bridget really resented that sentence and questioned how God could ask that of mothers He supposedly loved.

Katherine was actually waiting for Marlene to step in. Situations like these were generally where her friend shined. Marlene was an excellent facilitator, but in this case, Bridget was obviously not interested in being facilitated. She started before

Marlene even had a chance to intervene.

"Just last week all of you were in agreement that asking us to simply let go of our children was not only nearly impossible, it was cruel to even ask. But here you are, only seven days later, saying that some fiction book has brought you to the light!" Bridget threw her hands in the air and said, "That's ridiculous!"

Katherine was suddenly happy she hadn't had a chance to speak yet, but at the same time, her heart went out to Bridget. After all, she had felt exactly like Bridget only a few weeks ago. She wanted to reach out and hug her and tell her everything would be okay, but she also knew that would be a mistake, at least right then.

Before Katherine could do anything, Marlene did interject. "Did you finish the book, Bridget?"

"Yes," Bridget answered indignantly.

"And it brought you no comfort?" Marlene continued.

Bridget folded her arms across her chest. "No, not really. Sure, I cried at all the right parts, but at the end of the day, my boy is still lost, and I still can't do anything about it."

The woman began to cry in earnest then, and Katherine did put her arm around her.

Marlene seemed to recognize on some level what only good facilitators do, and that was not to pressure Bridget into talking. So instead, she turned the conversation back to the other ladies, gently leading them to share their thoughts and experiences about the book while Katherine simply held the quietly crying Bridget.

When Marlene finally said the closing prayer, the other women nervously left while Marlene, Katherine, and Bridget remained behind. Marlene and Katherine had a silent exchange that let Marlene know to leave the two women alone for a while.

After everyone was gone, Katherine leaned back and took her arm away from Bridget's shoulder.

"Bridget," she started, "would you like to go somewhere for coffee?"

Bridget looked up at her through puffy, tear-dimmed eyes and only nodded.

"Did you drive?" Katherine asked.

Bridget nodded again, and Katherine said, "Okay, how about we meet at Corner Coffee down the road on Peach and 12th Streets? Say, fifteen minutes?"

"Are you sure you even want to," Bridget asked. "Especially after the spectacle I just made of myself."

"You didn't make a spectacle of yourself, Bridget. You're hurting. We all know what that's like. I just figured you'd like to talk to someone."

"I would, yes."

"Then it's settled. I'll see you at Corner Coffee in fifteen."

"Okay. On my way."

Katherine didn't want to seem pushy, so she left Bridget alone to go when she felt like it. Besides, she was hoping she could catch Marlene in the parking lot before she left.

She hurried out to the parking lot and caught Marlene getting into her vehicle.

"Is she still crying?" Marlene asked when Katherine came alongside the car.

"No, she and I are going to have coffee."

"Wow, that's good, Kate. I thought it best not to put Bridget on the spot in front of all of those women at that moment. Maybe one-on-one time with you is just what the doctor ordered."

Katherine wasn't convinced. "Maybe so, Mar, but with me? I'm barely out of the woods she's lost in. How can I help her?"

Marlene smiled. "Exactly because of that. She'll hear you, Kate, when she wouldn't hear anyone else. She knows that you know how she's feeling. That makes you the perfect person to talk to her right now."

"If you say so," Katherine said, still unconvinced.

"I do say so. And I'll be praying for you, friend."

"Thanks, Mar. I have a feeling I'm going to need it."

"And Kate," Marlene said as Katherine turned to walk toward her own SUV. "I'm so proud of you."

"For what?"

"For your willingness to hear."

Katherine just smiled and blew a kiss to her friend. She walked to her SUV and pulled out of the parking lot toward Corner Coffee.

She prayed, "Lord, help me say the right things." Then she added, "And if Arella is free, can You send him along?"

As Katherine pulled in, she saw Bridget already sitting at a table near the window. She was fidgeting with her keys, looking very uncomfortable.

Katherine came in and went over to her. "Can I get you some coffee?"

"No, thank you," Bridget answered.

"Well, I'm going to get me a cup. I'll be right over."

Katherine ordered her usual, an Americano with a double shot of espresso. She wasn't sure why, but the added caffeine seemed necessary all of a sudden.

Once back at the table with Bridget, she sat down and noticed that her palms were sweating. Why was she so nervous? Oh, that's right. She didn't know what she was doing. How silly of her to forget.

"So, what's your son's name?" She was drawing a blank as to where to start, so small talk seemed like the logical thing.

"Cory."

"Hmmm. And how long has Cory been out of the military?"

"Oh, he's been out about ten years. But like I said, it feels like he never left. He's just not my Cory anymore."

"And you feel helpless because there's nothing you can do to help him?"

"Yeah, that about sums it up. I can't sleep, I can't eat, I'm miserable all the time, and my marriage has suffered because of it. I just can't seem to get over it. I want to do something to help him so badly, but there's nothing I can do."

"That's it, isn't it?" Katherine decided to take a chance and launch right in. "It's when we are in the position of 'no control.' We can't control a thing that happens with them, and it feels horrible."

Bridget was nodding, so Katherine took this as a sign that she could continue.

"Believe me, I know how that feels. My daughter, Nicole, is a drug addict. She's only twenty-five years old, but we lost her completely. She'd leave all of the time and then disappear for weeks, sometimes months at a time. We wouldn't usually hear from her until the hospital or one of her friends called. We'd go get her, but the cycle would just replay itself over and over again. She just recently came home after another bender."

Bridget was looking up at Katherine now, giving Katherine her full attention.

"I'm telling you, Bridget, I didn't think I could take it anymore. She wasn't my baby girl anymore, and even though we thought we had done all we could do for her, nothing seemed to work. And believe me, I tried everything."

Bridget nodded. "Yeah, me, too," she said.

"I was in complete despair, and like you, everything was suffering—my friendships, my marriage, my relationship with my son, and most importantly, my relationship with God. I blamed Him for what was happening. After all, God is big enough to put an end to it, so why wouldn't He? And why wouldn't He just tell me what to do to help her? It felt instead like God had left me out to hang by myself with no help from Him at all."

"Yes!" Bridget yelled, and she yelled loudly enough for the coffee patrons closest to them to turn quickly to see who interrupted their caffeine reverie.

"Sorry," she lowered her voice and then continued. "That's exactly it! Why won't God just tell me what to do to help Cory? He's my son! God gave him to me to take care of, so why won't He let me do that?"

Katherine said another silent prayer, asking God to give her the right words.

"Bridget, let me ask you a question. When Cory was going through boot camp, you knew he was going to go through a lot of physical pain, right? They were going to train him, yes, but they were also going to be sure that Cory could make it, emotionally and physically, during the war. Now, I know you hated thinking about that, but would you have gone through it for him, and then sent him to Afghanistan? Would you have done all the physical tests and gone through all of the physical and emotional pain for Cory so that he wouldn't have to endure it and then made him figure out stuff in Afghanistan?

"No, I don't guess so."

"Of course you wouldn't. You hated thinking of your son in any kind of discomfort, but you knew it was for his good, to keep him safe and ready for what he had to do in that foreign land. I think that's a lot like what God is calling us to as mothers, as parents, really. It's just hard for mothers because like we've said in the class, we were created not to do that. We were created to keep them from harm and pain. But there comes a time in their lives that the pain is necessary so that they can learn how to live. If we took all that away by shielding them all of the time, they'd never learn how to live in this world, and they'd be pulverized at the first sign of danger.

"Now let's take that a step further." Katherine went on. "In God's kingdom, our purpose here on this earth is to help build that kingdom. Once we've become a Christ-follower, our only job here is to help others see how to possess that same gift of eternity. We can do that in a bunch of different ways, but the way that is most successful is by our examples, the way we live our lives and share our journeys with others. I started to realize that my desire to shield Nicole from her own journey was taking away her story, a story that only she was meant to tell so that she could help others see God."

Katherine could have sworn that she was having some sort of out-of-body experience right then. Where were these words coming from? She truly felt like it was no longer her who was speaking, though it was her voice she heard. Then that voice started back up again.

"Reading Mother Abraham helped me to see not only that, but why that was so hard for me. God created me to do the opposite of that. I was actually created to keep Nicole from harm. Letting her move toward harm is one of the hardest things I've ever had to do. The comfort came when I realized that God called me to the hard part, and He also created me with the strength to do it. I now see the high call of mothers, of mine, and I see how much God honors me in trusting me with such an important task.

"The book also made me rest in how much God loves me, Nicole's mother, and how honored I am to be given the responsibility of raising her for Him. Because it's really all about God anyway, right? All of this," she gestured around the coffee shop, "is just where we are on the way to where we are going. The point is helping others find their way, too. As mothers, we have to allow God to give our children their own stories to do the same thing. And like the Lord told Sarah in the book, that takes a strength given only to mothers."

Katherine sat back in her chair and sighed. "Now, I don't know about you, but the 'why' in that really comforts me, even as I anguish over having to watch my children suffer as they learn."

"So, if I'm hearing you right," Bridget said, "Cory has a story to tell, but he won't be able to tell it if he never lives it. I have to get out of the way so that he and God figure that out."

"That pretty much sums it up, yes."

"And the pain I feel, this absolute torment I feel at watching this happen, is because I was created to do the opposite of that. Yet my 'high calling,' as they call it in the book, is denying my created nature to give my boy back to God so that God can build Cory's story."

"I couldn't have said it better myself."

"No, you said it better," Bridget laughed, "but I think I get it. I'm still hurting, and I don't see an end to that any time soon, but I guess you're also saying that's okay.

That's the way it's supposed to be."

"Yep. That's the way I understand it, and that understanding has brought me more peace than I thought possible.

"And you know what," Katherine continued, "this is now part of your story. There's going to be someone somewhere who is going to need to hear how you got through this." She sat back again and smiled. "I like how God does that."

"Well, I can't imagine God ever using me, but I guess I'm open to it."

Katherine took Bridget's hands in hers and said, "Just wait, my friend. God's not done with you yet."

24

CHAPTER TWENTY FOUR

(SIX MONTHS LATER)

"*M*om! Where are my basketball shorts?"

"They're in the drawer with the rest of your team outfits!"

"They're not 'outfits,' Mom!"

"Well, your team costumes, then."

"Sheesh, mom. They're uniforms!"

Katherine was smiling as she finished putting on her earrings. She loved teasing her son, especially when he employed his male genetic fault of looking for things in one spot and then when he couldn't find them, demanding that someone moved or lost them.

Tommy came downstairs about ten minutes later in his basketball uniform, shorts and all. Katherine walked in right after him. "I see you found them. Dare I ask where they were?"

"No."

Katherine laughed as she saw that Nicole was busy plating a second batch of pancakes. Ken was already seated at the kitchen table enjoying the first one.

Katherine came up behind her daughter and planted a kiss on the back of her head. "Thanks for making breakfast, sweetheart."

"No prob. I like making pancakes."

"You like eating pancakes," Tommy said as he threw a napkin at his sister. She turned faster than he thought she would and planted a warm pancake right on the side of his face.

"Hey!" he yelled. "You're wasting perfectly good food!" And then he promptly took a bite of it.

"No food is wasted around you, boy," Ken said with a smile.

Katherine stood in the corner of the kitchen and couldn't keep the smile from her face. It was so nice to have them all together again. It had been a long, difficult road, but things were looking up.

"How's school going, Nicole?" Ken asked his daughter through a mouthful of pancakes.

"It's good. The classes are a bit challenging, and sometimes it's hard to balance my treatment schedule with my class schedule, but that won't be forever. I'm just happy I was able to get in that outpatient treatment program here in Corner Mountain. Otherwise school wouldn't even have been a possibility for a year at least." Nicole brought the last plate of pancakes over to the table and took her seat next to her brother.

"You coming to my game later?" Tommy asked his sister. He tried to act like he didn't care one way or the other, but everyone knew that he was pretty sure the sun and moon set on his sister's shoulders.

"Wouldn't miss it, Pain," Nicole answered. "What sport are you in now, badminton?"

"Hardy har har," Tommy said as he shoved another huge fork of pancakes into his mouth. "What about you, Mom and Dad?"

"I'll be there as soon as I finish my last meeting," Ken said.

"I'll be there," Katherine answered. "I have a meeting scheduled for this morning, but that's it for the day."

"How's that going?" Nicole asked.

Katherine sat down. "Good, I think. I don't know. I'm still not sure why they asked me to do this. There has to be more qualified people who could do it."

Ken placed his hand on Katherine's arm and squeezed it lovingly. "Pastor

Carter asked you because you are the best person to do it."

One of the best things that had happened lately was the improvement in Katherine's relationship with her husband. Understanding that God had called mothers to this daunting task didn't mean He didn't also call fathers. What it did mean, however, was that mothers were going to suffer through it differently simply because they were mothers. That didn't mean that fathers loved less; they just loved differently. When Katherine finally understood this, she was able to look at Ken with a renewed love and devotion that had wiggled its way out of her heart for a long time.

They never actually talked about it, but Ken noticed, and he was grateful for the change. The "why" didn't seem to concern him so much.

Katherine patted his hand affectionately as she smiled at him and poured syrup on her pancakes.

Eventually, she was left in the kitchen alone. She'd promised Nicole that she would do the dishes so Nicole could spend a few minutes at the library studying before class.

She really was so surprised by the way things turned out. She would never in a million years have thought that she would be asked to lead a women's group at the church, especially not a women's group comprised of mothers in trauma. Apparently there was a huge need for someone to minister to these moms, and Pastor Carter came to Katherine.

He explained to her that he had gone to Susan who led the Women's Ministry at the church, and she recommended Katherine. Katherine was pretty sure that recommendation came by way of Marlene, but Marlene wouldn't own up to it. When Katherine asked her, she simply shrugged her shoulders and walked away.

But the truth was that Katherine had been meeting with many of the mothers one-on-one for some time, sharing with them what she had learned. It seemed like the more she talked to women, the more women asked to talk to her. She didn't feel qualified to help anyone, but she could tell them what she had been through and what

God had taught her through it. Mostly it seemed that these women needed to hear that they weren't alone in their struggles.

Katherine often thought of Arella and wondered if this was the journey he spoke of. He'd told her that she and her daughter had work to do and that their journeys would soon begin. She figured this had to be at least the beginning of hers. She wondered what Nicole's would be. Her daughter definitely seemed to want to pursue a career in counseling, so maybe that would be it. She didn't know exactly, but whatever it was, she knew that God would do it.

Life was so much easier now that she rested in that. Sure, she was still Nicole's mother. She was Tommy's mother, and as their mother, she worried and fussed over them. However, she had more and more begun to be able to trust God with them, finding out step by step what it looked like to give her children back to their rightful Father. There was peace in the process, as hard as it was sometimes.

Katherine gathered her Bible and study materials and went out to the car. She pulled out of the driveway, and just as she was about to round the corner onto Main St., she could have sworn she saw a man standing at the corner of the last house on the right, a man with piercing blue eyes. She stopped in the middle of the street and backed up a few feet to have a better look, but no one was there.

Katherine smiled a little. She knew she didn't actually need to talk to Arella, or even see him for that matter. It was enough to know that he was there, watching over her and her family. He was there because her Father sent him to watch over them. That made Katherine smile even bigger.

She eventually pulled into the parking lot of Corner Mountain Community Church. She made her way back to a small classroom in the annex where a group of women were waiting for her expectantly. Since they were on winter break from school, Katherine had the time for these midweek classes until she went back to her regular teaching job after the holidays.

She put down her briefcase and took out the book, now worn on both the outside and inside from much reading. Katherine looked briefly at the cover, at the woman dressed in ambiguous Middle Eastern garb, and smiled. They really do need a different cover, she thought with a grin.

Then she looked up at the women and said, "Welcome to this book study. The book we will be reading is called Mother Abraham, but before I say another word, let me just say, we are Mother Abraham."

Katherine looked around the room where a dozen or so pairs of eyes looked at her with both confusion and expectation. Thank You, Father, Katherine suddenly thought. Thank You for everything.

Katherine smiled. In another part of town, the blue-eyed man smiled, and with him the Father smiled.

Arella walked down the sidewalk toward Corner Mountain Community College, and thoughts of seeing Nicole made him smile even bigger.

He really did love the journey.

DEBWATERBURY.COM

The FREE Bible study for

MOTHER ABRAHAM

-- the story of Sarah's struggle to let Isaac go --

is available now.

Download your free copy at debwaterbury.com/motherabraham

or simply click the link below or scan the barcode

with your device to download the PDF.

project Malonda
ONE WOMAN / ONE BUSINESS AT A TIME

ABOUT THE AUTHOR

Dr. Deb currently lives in Tucson, Arizona, with her husband, Jeff, and their dog, Levi. She has two adult sons, Spence and Miles, both of whom are steadily moving toward God's work in their own lives. Dr. Deb is the President and CEO of Deb Waterbury, LLC, which encompasses both her conferences and books, as well as her non-profit, Love Everlasting Ministries.

Love Everlasting Ministries is the umbrella corporation for her schools in Malawi, Africa. Among these schools is the Reap What You Sew School for impoverished women in Blantyre, Malawi, and Project Malonda, a more comprehensive trade school for women. Project Malonda is also located in Blantyre, Malawi.

The Reap What You Sew School for Women is a benevolent school that offers six months of training in the trade of tailoring, as well as two weeks of business training. At the end of the six months, each qualifying student will receive the sewing machine she has been sewing on, as well as enough cloth and other materials to begin her own tailoring business. Project Malonda is a larger training academy, offering training in tailoring, cosmetology, and culinary arts.

By helping women provide for themselves and their children, Dr. Deb says that, "We will help change women, their children, their villages, and finally, their nations." For more information on how you can be involved in sponsoring this school, as well as being personally connected to one of the students, please visit www.projectmalonda.org today.

Dr. Deb also hosts two weekly podcasts, "Real Life with Deb Waterbury" and "Get Real with Deb Waterbury" with new episodes premiering every Tuesday and Thursday. Both of these are available on YouTube, iTunes, and Spotify.

Dr. Deb is also available for conferences, book signings, and retreats. Simply contact her on her website, www.DebWaterbury.com, where you can email her and also see her other books, podcasts, blogs, and messages available for purchase or download.

lovetruthlive

WITH DEB WATERBURY

Teaching that the
love of Christ and
the truth of
Scripture lead to
life-changing
freedom.

"By this all people
will know that you
are my disciples,
if you have love
for one another."
- John 13:35

PAINTED WINDOW TRILOGY
PAINTED WINDOW, THREADS, AND WHITE ZEPHYR

Follow Elizabeth Percy's allegorical Journey into discovering
the love that transforms all of our lives - the love of Jesus,
our Bridegroom.

JAMES ON THE MOUNT

A study of the book of James as it relates to the
Sermon on the Mount

DAILY DEVOTIONAL SERIES
GALATIANS
EPHESIANS
PHILIPPIANS

3 month, Bible devotional studies, verse by verse

WOMEN'S MINISTRY STUDIES

6 PAIRS OF SANDALS

Yesterday's Footsteps and Today's Women's Ministry

THE LIES THAT BIND
AND THE TRUTH THAT SETS YOU FREE

Dr. Deb Waterbury gets real in The Lies that Bind, a very candid look into her own life as she exposes five specific lies that Satan told her about who she was and how those lies derailed her well into adulthood. How can we break those bonds and what truths must we replace those lies with once we expose them to the light of truth?

DR. DEB WATERBURY

Also offers:

Two Weekly Podcasts

"Real Life with Deb Waterbury"

&

"Get Real with Deb Waterbury"

Available on YouTube, iTunes, and Spotify

Visit us on Facebook, Twitter, Instagram, LinkedIn,
Pinterest and YouTube

Note:

Dr. Deb Waterbury continues to expand her resource catalogue, so please log into her website for the most recent additions.